MINE WARFARE ON LAND

Also available from Brassey's

Brassey's Multilingual Military Dictionary

BELLAMY
Red God of War: Soviet Artillery and Rocket Forces

FARRAR & LEEMING
Military Ballistics — A Basic Manual

GOAD & HALSEY
Ammunition (including Grenades and Mines)

LAFFIN
Brassey's Battles: 3,500 Years of Conflict, Campaigns and Wars from A–Z

LEE ET AL.
Guided Weapons (including Light, Unguided Anti-Tank Weapons)

MYLES
Jump Jet, 2nd Edition

RYAN
Guns, Mortars and Rockets

MINE WARFARE ON LAND

by

LIEUTENANT-COLONEL C. E. E. SLOAN, RE

With a Foreword by
GENERAL SIR NIGEL BAGNALL, GCB, CVO, MC, ADC Gen

BRASSEY'S DEFENCE PUBLISHERS
A Member of the Pergamon Group

LONDON · OXFORD · WASHINGTON DC
NEW YORK · TORONTO · SYDNEY · FRANKFURT

UK (Editorial)	Brassey's Defence Publishers Ltd., Maxwell House, 74 Worship Street, London EC2A 2EN
(Orders & Enquiries)	Brassey's Defence Publishers Ltd., Headington Hill Hall, Oxford OX3 0BW, England
USA (Editorial)	Pergamon-Brassey's International Defense Publishers, 1340 Old Chain Bridge Road, McLean, Virginia 22101, USA
(Orders & Enquiries)	Pergamon Press Inc., Maxwell House, Fairview Park, Elmsford, New York 10523, USA
CANADA	Pergamon Press Canada Ltd., Suite 104, 150 Consumers Road, Willowdale, Ontario M2J 1P9, Canada
AUSTRALIA	Pergamon Press (Aust.) Pty. Ltd., PO Box 544, Potts Point, NSW 2011, Australia
FEDERAL REPUBLIC OF GERMANY	Pergamon Press GmbH, Hammerweg 6, D-6242 Kronberg, Federal Republic of Germany
JAPAN	Pergamon Press Ltd., 8th Floor, Matsuoka Central Building, 1-7-1 Nishishinjuku, Shinjuku-ku, Tokyo 160, Japan
BRAZIL	Pergamon Editora Ltda., rue Eca de Queiros, 346, CEP 04011, São Paulo, Brazil
PEOPLE'S REPUBLIC OF CHINA	Pergamon Press, Qianmen Hotel, Beijing, People's Republic of China

First edition 1986

Library of Congress Cataloging in Publication Data
Sloan, C. E. E.
Minewarfare on land.
Bibliography: p.
Includes index.
1. Mines, Military. I. Title.
UG490.S55 1985 358'.3 85-24309

British Library Cataloguing in Publication Data
Sloan, C. E. E.
Minewarfare on land.
1. Mines, Military
I. Title
623.4'5115'09 UG490

ISBN 0-08-031196-2

Printed in Great Britain by A. Wheaton & Co. Ltd., Exeter

Foreword

In peacetime it is all too easy to underplay the significance of mines. To the crew of a 50-ton tank travelling at best speed, white tape and an umpire more concerned for his personal safety than representing the effectiveness of his obstacle, mines present no problem. Given some live mines and the same crew, the situation would be very different. Dash would be replaced by caution, determination by prudence and contempt by a healthy respect. The psychological effect of mines is then a factor of considerable importance in itself.

Mines are relatively inexpensive, and can be laid in advance of combat, thus allowing the most economical use to be made of scarce engineer resources. As this book recalls, they caused a large proportion of tank casualties in World War II and more recent conflicts, and technological advances are making them increasingly lethal. Yet they can be a double-edged weapon. A Warsaw Pact attack in the Central Region of NATO could not be defeated by a purely static defence. Our own forces must be capable of conducting counter-offensive operations to destroy enemy penetrations. As Lieutenant Colonel Sloan rightly points out, the requirements of reserve formations must be taken into account, and our own defensive minefields must not impede the mobility of our reserves.

Cedric Sloan has written a thoughtful book in which he concentrates on mines, or those "sinister and dangerous devices", as he so aptly calls them. He traces the development of mine warfare — before going on to consider what the future may bring in a manner that is both perceptive and thought-provoking. He has made a useful contribution to an area of military study which professional officers of all Arms would be ill advised to neglect.

General Sir Nigel Bagnall

Acknowledgements

THE preparation of this book would have been impossible without the help and advice of many people. To all of them I wish to offer my thanks. In particular, I am most grateful to the companies and establishments, which have provided information on mine warfare equipment. If there are errors in fact amongst the product details and specifications, then I apologize, for they will be my mistakes and not those of the persons who so kindly responded to my requests for information. I am indebted to Brigadier Francis Sugden and Major Charles Moorhouse for their close reading of the text and to Mr. John Jeffrey for his practical help throughout. I would also like to express my gratitude to General Sir Nigel Bagnall, who so readily agreed to write the Foreword.

Although I am a serving officer, and held an appointment in the Ministry of Defence during the writing of the book, this is neither an official work nor a statement of policy. The opinions, arguments and interpretation are mine, for which I alone am responsible. The book represents a personal view of mine warfare, based upon an examination of unclassified sources and upon my own limited experience. Writing the book has been an instructive and enjoyable pursuit, if time-consuming. That time was found at the expense of my family. I wish to close, therefore, by thanking Susie, my wife, for her acceptance of my self-indulgence, and for her patient typing of every word that I have written.

Contents

List of Figures

List of Plates

List of Plates

Between pages 94 and 95

1

Introduction

GUNPOWDER is a rare commodity these days, but in its time a revolutionary substance, which gave rise to cannon, musket and bomb. By the end of the seventeenth century military engineers, recognizing the destructive power of this dangerous black powder, had also devised a scheme for exploiting its explosive force in siege warfare. If the unfortunate defenders of a besieged fortification refused to submit, an entry would be forced through a breach in the walls. The technique which evolved to achieve this breach, involved sapping and mining. A zig-zag trench, or sap, would be dug towards the wall or gate to be destroyed. The sappers, a name by which military engineers are still known, eventually reached a point below the area of the desired breach, where an enormous gunpowder charge would be detonated. Methods of using explosives in this way were studied, refined and recorded as experience grew during the eighteenth and nineteenth centuries. A comprehensive, but now rare, treatise on these mining techniques was prepared in 1776 by Professor M. J. M. Geuss under the title of: *Théorie de L'Art du Mineur.*

Not surprisingly, the practice of mining beneath enemy lines was continued during the trench battles of World War I. In 1915, half a million kilograms of ammonal explosive shattered the German trench network on Vimy Ridge. A similar amount was stealthily mined into the Messines Ridge over a subsequent period of 2 years. When it was detonated the ridge virtually disappeared. In the same year, 1917, the first major success for a brand new weapon, the tank, took place. At Cambrai, British Tank Corps units achieved a surprise victory over entrenched German troops heralding the arrival of the most potent, conventional weapon seen on the battlefield to this day. The foundations of mechanized warfare had been laid.

An effective means of dealing with these new and terrifying landships had to be found, and the ever-resourceful German troops developed a suitable counter: the mine. This descendant of siege mining originally consisted of either an artillery shell, buried base down with its fuze at surface height, or a wooden box packed with explosive and detonated by a modified grenade fuze. Against the light armour and crude tracks of early vehicles, these devices were very effective. Nevertheless, by 1918, anti-tank mines had developed into prepared munitions in their own right. A new weapon, the contact mine, had entered the military inventory.

This book is centred upon that weapon. A sinister and dangerous device, it has tended to be viewed as a specialist weapon. Normally the responsibility of combat engineers or assault pioneers, the anti-tank mine is rarely publicized or displayed. Yet, for a fraction of the cost of a main battle tank, it can wreak devastating damage upon that million dollar machine. Never holding the general appeal of a gun or rifle, an anti-personnel fragmentation mine can as easily decimate an infantry squad as a machine gun, but without the expense, training and logistics associated with small arms. For these reasons, mine warfare has become a standard component of guerrilla war, and the mine a terrorist tool. Thus no army or security force, of whatever size, in whatever area, can afford to ignore mines or counter-measures to them.

It is estimated that 20 per cent of tank losses in World War II (WWII) can be attributed to mines, in Vietnam this rose to some 70 per cent of US armour casualties. Since then, warhead efficiency, sensing devices, speed of laying and modes of delivery have all improved. The threat from mines is greater than ever. The present, existing series of mines are referred to as second generation, the third generation will be in service by the end of the century. Their appearance will be as different from that of the conventional anti-tank mine, as the latter is from the siege sap of the seventeenth century. The application of new technology, primarily in the fields of intelligent fuzing and remote delivery, will make mines ever more effective and increasingly difficult to defeat. This book will seek to chronicle those developments.

We shall start our review of mine warfare with an examination of several conflicts, illustrating the use of mines. This will bring us to the present and an assessment of the role that the mine has to play in modern combat. The various types of mine required will then be discussed, showing available models and typical usage. An up-date on mine technology will be included prior to an analysis of mine counter-measures. Finally, a look into the future will be attempted, forecasting the threats to be countered by third generation mines and what form those mines might take.

This book was prepared to promote a greater understanding of mine warfare — both within armed forces and amongst a more general readership. It is an aspect of war that is greatly underestimated in peace, yet frighteningly effective in combat. Mine awareness is the controlled military term for this effect. The knowledge that mines are in the area immediately provokes caution, operations slow down, a reluctance to advance is apparent. Thus mines are as much a psychological weapon as a physical one. This attack on the mind must be countered by knowledge and training. It is to be hoped that the following chapters will provide the foundation for that knowledge.

2

Mine Warfare of Recent Times

World War II

Prior to World War II, few nations of the industrial world gave proper consideration to advances in military thought or equipment. Mechanized warfare was neglected along with other aspects of the armed forces. It took crushing defeats from Blitzkrieg in Europe, and Afrika Korps successes in Libya, to accentuate the rising importance of tanks in battle. The outcome of this was a pressing necessity to develop an effective defence against armour, for the great majority of troops continued to fight on foot. So began the accelerating interest in anti-tank mines, their concentration into minefields and their protection by anti-personnel mines or anti-lift devices. The Eighth Army mine school on the Nile Delta evolved drills for the laying and breaching of minefields, which formed the basis for British mine warfare practice — in all future theatres of the war. Axis and Allied munition factories geared-up production to meet the escalating demand for every variety of mine and massive minefields became a common feature of any defence plan. In North Africa it was not uncommon to find minefields several miles deep.

Yet even these vast expanses, sowed liberally with all manner of fiendish device, were overshadowed by the scale of Soviet employment of mines. It is claimed that the Russians laid in excess of 200 million mines throughout the war with Germany. In their preparations for the great tank battle at Kursk alone, they are reputed to have prepared minefields with a density of 4000 mines per mile of front. Nor were all of these mines simple, crude devices. By 1942 the Soviets had developed a remote-control mine, which could be detonated by a radio code at precisely the time required. But the Russians themselves were also victims of advances in mine development. It was the Finns who, in their defensive battle against the Communist invader, appear to have used ice mines for the first time. Normally command-detonated, these were originally bottle-shaped explosive charges, suspended below the ice covering lakes or rivers, and designed to crack the frozen surface so that men or vehicles could not then move safely across.

In warmer climes the Italian Army was one of the first to realize that the detection of mines would be made more difficult, and breaching that much slower and dangerous, by minimizing the metal content of mines. Whilst the powerful German Tellermines, and the slightly smaller British MkV anti-tank mines, continued to be manufactured from sheet metal, filled with Amatol or TNT, the Italians made the casing of the Pignone mine from bakelite. In the rugged terrain of the Italian Campaign the avenues of advance for tracked and wheeled vehicles

3

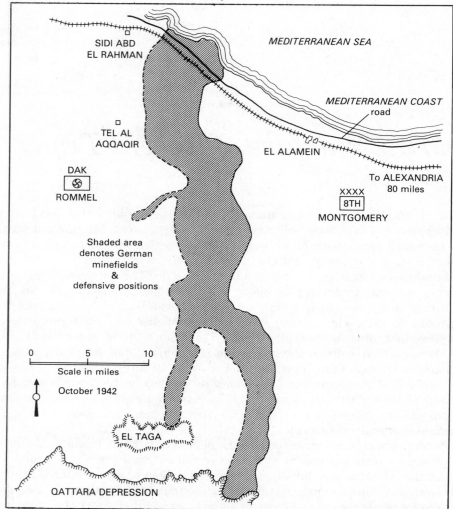

FIG. 2.1. *German minefields at El Alamein — a formidable obstacle.*

were severely limited by natural features. These restrictions on mobility allowed even greater importance to be placed on the use of mines by the defending Wehrmacht troops. By sowing at random along the verges of tracks or roads, in the rubble of demolished bridges or on the banks of rivers near likely crossing sites, they succeeded in causing almost 30 per cent of the Allied tank casualties through mines alone.

Mining activities in the war against Japan followed much the same pattern as in Italy, except this time under tropical conditions and in even more difficult terrain. There were fewer roads, yet their very scarcity made them vital to the support of defender and attacker alike, becoming a prime target for mining and ambush. Anti-personnel mines took on a new significance as the protagonists penetrated the jungles on footpaths or mule tracks. The mine, a silent, unattended weapon with a long-life, could be left concealed, to guard a track junction for days or weeks with the intention of wounding and delaying those who attempted to pass. In any situation where available manpower was insufficient to cover every approach, mines could be used to good effect in closing routes, protecting beaches and defending airstrips. The Japanese, in fact, went so far as to convert torpedo warheads into massive land mines to deny island airfields to the American task forces.

Vietnam

During the many conflicts arising in the post-war years, mines continued to be used and countered. In particular, the Vietnam War provides an exceptionally useful study into the utility of mines. Major-General George S. Patton, after commanding troops in Vietnam, considered that, of all the weapons used against armoured units, mines were the greatest cause for concern.

Casualty figures support General Patton's view on mines. One estimate places the percentage of US armour lost from mine attack at 70 per cent of the total of all losses from enemy action. French experience in Indo China shows an even higher figure of 85 per cent of their tank losses being specifically attributed to Communist mines. Naturally, these statistics were so high because the wet or tangled terrain of Vietnam tended to channel heavy armoured vehicles on to the road network. The Viet Cong became masters of the convoy ambush, halting the lead vehicles with remotely detonated mines and raking the follow-up vehicles with RPG7 and small arms fire. Nuisance mining, through carefully concealed pressure mines hidden in the roads or at likely stopping places, also created a fearful respect for mines amongst the US Army and Marine Corps units.

In response, improved detection devices and a variety of counter-measure equipment, such as mine rollers, were introduced. Means of blast-proofing the M113 armoured personnel carrier (APC) were attempted too. The US troops used their ingenuity and improved their own protection by sand-bagging floors and driver seats. All of these precautions helped, and tank crew casualties were never high as a result of anti-vehicle mines. The real losses were felt in terms of damaged or destroyed equipment and an increased logistic load. Tracks and running gear on the heavier vehicles were usually the major components to be replaced and refitted, imposing an extra burden on the supply chain, the repair teams and crew time in tank units.

The effect on APCs or amphibians was quite different. Being much lighter than a gun tank, the carrier could, and on occasions was, thrown on to its back by the force of the mine exploding. Equally, if there was penetration of the vehicle by hot gasses or metal spall, the interior compartment inevitably became a scene of charred carnage. Troops often preferred to travel on top of, rather than inside, their APCs for this very reason.

Another form of transport used extensively by the US forces in Vietnam was the helicopter and this too became a target for the Viet Cong mine. Whilst the normal tactic would be to attack the troops on deplaning, some attempts were made to damage the helicopters themselves by means of DH-10 fragmentation mines. Similar to the Western Claymore mine, the directional DH-10 device would be triggered to attack the machines as they hovered close to the ground. The development of the anti-helicopter mine had its origins in this conflict.

Arab-Israeli Wars

The predominant weapon within the Israeli land forces is the main battle tank. This is an inevitable outcome of their emphasis on mobile warfare, resulting from the extensive border they share with Arab neighbours. To lay effective minefields along the entire border would be prohibitively expensive and could never guarantee protection from determined breaching operations. The Israeli concept of operations, therefore, has been one of concentrating force to meet identified incursions rather than holding ground everywhere. Consequently, mine warfare has not played a major part in their military activity and has been poorly reported upon. Yet there are still lessons to be gained from the experiences of mine warfare in Arab-Israeli conflicts.

Two incidents in 1956 illustrated the power of minefields to halt or delay mechanized forces. In the battle for Alm Ageila, a company of Israeli half-tracks was easily put out of action as the vehicles attempted to drive through an Egyptian minefield at Um Katef. Those that were not immobilized by mines were immediately selected for destruction by anti-tank weapons. At Khan Yunis, a Palestinian Brigade had protected its position with a minefield containing plastic mines. Knowing how difficult it would be to detect and lift these devices, and not having the time to do so, an Israeli combat group of Patton and Centurion tanks drove straight on to the minefield. The assault was eventually successful, but the momentum of the attack became severely degraded as tracks were blown off and the unit fighting strength dwindled.

A more deliberate clearance operation, from the same Sinai campaign, illustrates the limitations of hand breaching minefields. As part of the general task of removing Egyptian forces from the Gaza Strip it was necessary to overcome a strong brigade position at Rafah, a communications focus for road and rail. The southern flank of the Egyptian position was protected by three minefield belts, only two of which were known to the Israeli assault force. The minefields stretched for about 5 kilometres, were some 50 metres deep and the first two were 300 metres apart. Twenty-four hours prior to the attack, mine breaching parties slipped into the minefields under cover of darkness. Through both minefields they cleared three paths, each 9 metres wide and separated by about 150 metres. Despite extreme care to conceal the Israeli breaching activities, on the following day it was observed that Egyptian troops were working in the minefields close to two of the breached areas. The obvious assumption was made that only one gap could still be considered to be free from mines. Thus plans were changed and the two assault battalions squeezed through the one breach that night.

Unknown to the advancing infantry, the third minefield lay waiting undetected, unbreached. First one, then two, then three half-tracks hit mines, the column behind halting as illuminating shells caught the damaged vehicles in their flares. Defending anti-tank guns soon had the stranded vehicles burning fiercely in the night sky, affording an unwelcome glow for the Israeli sappers to see and be seen by. Under sporadic artillery fire, these quickly-assembled breaching parties groped forward, detecting, lifting and removing mines. By dawn the force had pierced the obstacle and moved on to their objectives, albeit well behind schedule.

Attempting, without complete success, to drive through minefields, not knowing what obstacles were ahead, and resorting to hand-breaching, were experiences that both sides had noted and were determined to learn from. When the Syrians stormed the Israeli positions on the Golan in 1973, their armoured forces were preceded through mined areas by four, sometimes five, flail tanks in line abreast — exploding the mines before them. Later in the war, as fortunes changed and the Israeli counter-attack in the West was forcing a corridor through the Egyptian forces, a minefield was put to unusual and interesting use. The Egyptian 25th Armoured Brigade, comprising nearly 100 T-62 tanks, was driving along the eastern bank of the Great Bitter Lake in an attempt to take the Israeli force from a flank. But they had been seen. They were ambushed from their own right flank and driven on to one of the original Israeli defensive minefields. Caught between mines and the tank guns of two opposing brigades, the 25th Brigade lost 86 tanks and every one of its APCs. Rather than being used as a protective barrier, on this occasion the minefield was used as the anvil for an armoured hammer.

To prevent themselves being caught in a similar position, and to enable attacks through minefields, which had been so expensive in time and resources in 1967, the Israelis had developed mine ploughs for rapid breaching by the time of the Yom Kippur War. They were also required to continue to improve their counter-mine capability after the war, as Arab terrorists adopted a tactic of nuisance mining, particularly within the northern border area. The mines could appear anywhere, one boy was killed when a football field at Dishon was mined, and roads near the frontiers had to be swept for mines prior to their first use in the morning. Arising from these experiences detection and disposal techniques have been well formulated in the Israeli Defence Forces.

The Falklands War

As a consequence of the many small wars and counter-insurgency operations, in which they have been involved since 1945, British troops have also built up a notable experience in mine warfare techniques. These skills were sorely needed for operations against the Argentinian forces on the Falklands in 1982.

Over the two months that they were in occupation of the Falkland Islands, the Argentinians laid extensive minefields in those coastal areas where they anticipated a British force might land. These areas tended to be the obvious landing sites close to the town and port of Stanley. Despite some lack of co-ordination between the Argentinian Marine and Army engineers, the minefields were competently laid, recorded and fenced. But after the British Task Force had landed at an unexpected point, and threatened the defences of Stanley from the West, there began a spate of random, poorly recorded and inadequately marked mining by Argentinian forces. These mined areas proved a problem, both during the conflict, as British troops encountered them without warning, and after the cease-fire when they had to be cleared or fenced.

During the actions in the mountains above Stanley some attempts were made to breach routes through identified minefields in preparation for attacks on the Argentinian positions. This was the case near Mount Harriet, where a poorly fenced, rapidly emplaced, minefield lay across 42 Royal Marine Commando's approach route to their objective. The minefield had been identified only after a Marine reconnaissance patrol had taken a casualty from an anti-personnel mine. The patrol extricated itself from the mined area using knives and bayonets as mine prodders, a task which took most of the night. To enable 42 Commando to reach the start line for its attack, a path through the minefield had to be cleared. This was successfully undertaken by Sappers from 3 Commando Brigade in pitch darkness, under freezing conditions, slowly by hand. Elsewhere, assault units sometimes did not know where Argentinian mines had been laid until they were actually fighting through them. On Mount Longdon the battle began when an NCO of the 3rd Battalion, The Parachute Regiment stepped on a mine and drew the first Argentinian fire of that battle. Nor were Scorpion light armoured vehicles of The Blues and Royals immune, one being severely damaged during a diversionary attack south of Tumbledown.

Yet these mines remain a problem, years after the cease-fire. The inability to detect the more modern devices, such as the Italian SB33 anti-personnel mine; the inadequate marking of mined areas; the lack of minefield records; the scattering of mines without regard to mine laying drills or patterns; and the unpleasant tendency of mines to move in sand or peat, as a result of wind or drainage flow, were all factors which contributed to the massive problem facing British engineers tasked with the identification, marking and clearance of minefields on the Falkland Islands. Parachute, Commando and Gurkha sappers were employed on these tasks, supported in the early stages by Argentinian prisoners who had volunteered to assist them. Once the areas offering the greatest danger to the public had been cleared, the priority became one of locating and fencing mined areas, whilst a safe and effective method of clearance could be developed. This proved to be neither a quick nor simple task to achieve.

The Hidden Menace

This very brief summary, of but a few years, has illustrated the continuing requirement for mines in battle and the need to have means of overcoming them. The mine has a part to play at every level of conflict, in any terrain, against, a variety of targets. It can take many forms, varying from a crude, improvised device to a complex weapon that is not easily detected or neutralized. Far from being outmoded, the mine has developed in phase with its primary target, the battle tank. It has also displayed a high degree of adaptability, limited only by the ingenuity and imagination of the user. With a psychological impact in addition to its physical effect, the mine is an inexpensive weapon, which remains a potent force on the battlefield. How that force can be harnessed to best tactical effect is proposed in the next chapter.

PLATE 1.1. *The earth's surface begins to rupture at the moment of detonation of a World War I landmine.*

PLATE 2.1. *A team of British soldiers use prodders and a Canadian mine detector to clear this Athens street during World War II.*

PLATE 2.2. *A Japanese anti-tank mine improvised from a 500 kilogram bomb.*

PLATE 2.3. *A selection of mines used by Argentinian forces on the Falkland Islands.*

PLATE 4.1. *Handlaying a first generation anti-tank mine.*

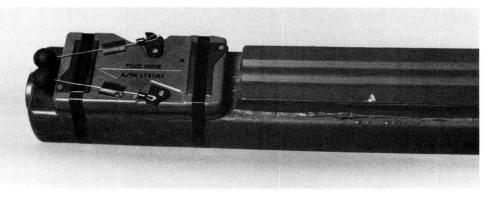

PLATE 4.2. *The anti-disturbance fuze fitted to Barmine.*

PLATE 4.3. *A second generation, hollow charge, influence fuzed, anti-tank mine.*

PLATE 4.4. *Lawmine — a concept model for the second generation, enhanced off route mine.*

PLATE 4.5. *The Barmine layer allows rapid mine dispensing, whilst the crew remain under armour protection.*

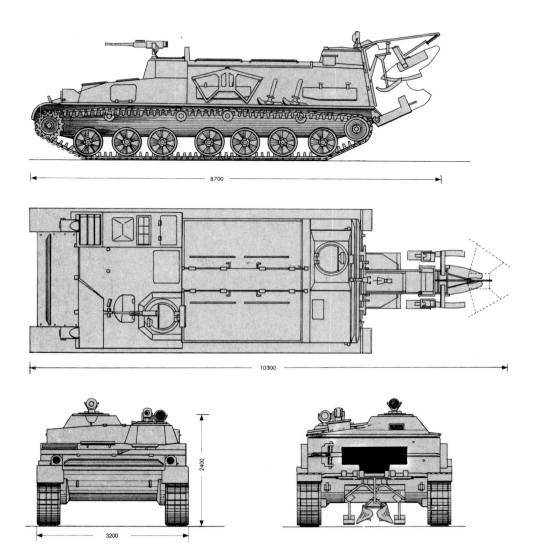

PLATE 4.6. *The Soviet GMZ armoured mine layer.*

PLATE 4.7. *On-board, scatterable mine dispensers in action.*

PLATE 4.8. *A helicopter scatterable mine system for rapid laying of anti-armour obstacles.*

PLATE 4.9. *The modern mine layer — a 155-millimetre self-propelled howitzer capable of delivering mines out to a range of 20 kilometres.*

PLATE 4.10. *A vehicle-mounted, scatterable mine system from Italy.*

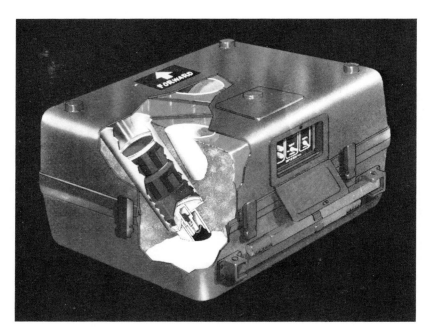

PLATE 4.11. *MOPMS — an interesting concept for this early generation area defence weapon.*

PLATE 4.12. *A mine launcher for infantry close protection tasks, with a possible role in rapid deployment forces.*

3

Mines in a Tactical Setting

Defence Options

THERE are two primary forms of military action, offence and defence. Mine warfare has been most closely associated with the defence, and we shall pursue that relationship further. In deciding how to defend his area of responsibility, the commander must choose between positional or mobile defence. To make such a decision he will undertake a tactical appreciation, which, in essence, is a methodical and logical examination of all those factors that may affect his plan. Enemy strength, own resources, the terrain, time available, and state of training, are just some of the parameters he will consider. But a strong influence on his ultimate decision will be a personal belief in the effectiveness of either form of defence.

Positional defence is a concept losing favour amongst those nations with highly mechanized forces, especially those which have limitations on the manpower available to them. It requires the physical occupation of ground and immediate protection of likely enemy targets. It is extremely expensive in personnel and equipment, such that reserves are at a minimum, unable to reinforce those areas under greatest threat or to react to an unexpected enemy action. If sufficient resources are available in strength to dominate the area being defended, positional defence can be extremely effective. But few countries have the forces to fully protect all likely enemy approaches and objectives.

"Maginot Line Mentality" is a by-product of positional defence. This attitude causes the defender to believe that he simply needs to construct a strong perimeter position, well protected, with the maximum of troops in prepared trenches and bunkers. Any attempt to breach this forward defence will, of course, be repelled by the fire power brought to bear on the selected killing ground. Sadly, history is full of impregnable fortifications being over-run or by-passed. The British Task Force recapture of the Falkland Islands is the most recent example of many. The small force, comprising 3 Commando and 5 Infantry Brigade, did not land on the mined beaches overlooked by battalions of Argentinians armed with heavy machine guns, cannon and howitzers. They approached from an unexpected direction, dislocated the defence and overcame much greater numbers than themselves. In other circumstances, the attacker could concentrate his own forces to be superior at a particular point to the defender. Overwhelming the defence at that point he forces an entry through the protective perimeter, allowing the attacking troops to break-through into the less protected depth of the area. Nowadays, this breach can be most easily effected through the use of chemical or nuclear weapons.

9

TYPES OF MINEFIELD

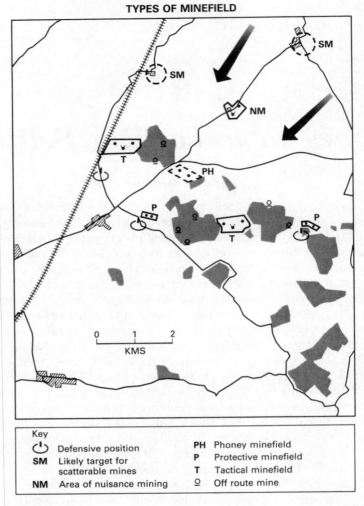

Key

(') Defensive position   **PH** Phoney minefield

SM Likely target for   **P** Protective minefield
scatterable mines   **T** Tactical minefield

NM Area of nuisance mining   ○ Off route mine

FIG. 3.1. *Types of minefield — possible uses of the various minefields.*

If positional defence is characterized by committing the majority of troops to static occupation, with few reserves, then mobile defence is quite the opposite. The minimum of troops will be employed in defending absolutely vital ground, leaving many more as mobile reserves. They remain well back from the border, or front line, or Forward Edge of the Battle Area (FEBA), in dispersed, concealed positions ready to react to the most dangerous enemy moves. But mobile defence does not mean brash attacks by lines of MBT (Main Battle Tanks) firing on the move. The mobility refers to a tactical flexibility, that allows the reserve to move to a well considered position following assessment of the enemy's intentions. At this position the enemy is engaged by the now static defender, who surprises the intruder in a large scale ambush. However, mobile defence is not restricted to armoured forces. Troops can be carried by support helicopters to the required position, or forced marches could achieve the same effect in forested areas, or ATGW (Anti-Tank Guided Weapon) helicopters can be used in conjunction with artillery and ground attack aircraft to destroy enemy thrusts.

Nevertheless, no defence will be completely positional or mobile. Within a principally positional defence, the reserves must be able to respond in the same reactive way as those operating under mobile defence. Troops occupying important positions as part of the framework for mobile defence, will base their defensive layout on the principles of strong positional defence, whilst the reserves carry out counter-moves.

Counter-moves

There are a variety of actions, which reserves can undertake. Each meets a unique requirement and would need to use or overcome mines in specific ways. The best known counter-move is the counter-attack, being the re-occupation of lost positions or ground. To counter-attack, the assault group may have to breach their own, original protective minefields, and after the assault, reinstate or reinforce those minefields. Counter-penetration is the term used to describe a manoeuvre, deploying a force from its hide location to a pre-planned, blocking position. This is chosen, on the basis of the best available intelligence reports, to hold enemy incursions. Mines are used within this blocking position and to protect the flanks or rear of the counter-penetration force. The counter-penetration could well be used in conjunction with a counter-stroke. This can be visualized as a sweep through an advancing enemy to disrupt his momentum, destroy part of his force and create panic within his chain of command. Thus, whilst the armoured vanguard of an enemy thrust would be held by the counter-penetration position, the counter-stroke would be delivered from a flank to the less formidable follow-up forces. To reach their start point for the counter-stroke, the force may have to breach their own minefields, and as they launch the attack they may have to breach mines laid by the enemy to protect his flank. Equally, the commander of the counter-stroke units will be concerned to ensure that his own force is not surprised and attacked during its slash through the enemy column. In order to protect this action, he may use reconnaissance troops for surveillance to his flanks and order mines to be laid across vulnerable areas on those flanks. The most ambitious manoeuvre is the counter-offensive. This is a major undertaking by a large force to restore the integrity of a defended area. To breach minefields in the advance, to lay protective minefields *en route* and to scatter mines amongst the withdrawing enemy would be some of the mine-warefare abilities expected of the counter-offensive force.

Design for Battle

Assuming that mobile defence will be used as the tactical concept, it is possible to offer a general design for battle that can be applied to most situations, to be tuned finely to specific circumstances. It would be normal to expect the defended area to be sectioned into three zones: the delay zone, the main battle zone, and the support area.

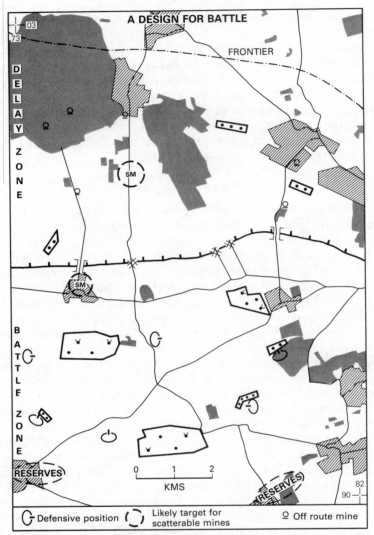

Fig. 3.2. *A design for battle — the obstacle framework for a mobile defence.*

A delay zone would be defended by no more than one-third of the fighting troops. It is the area closest to the enemy and its purpose is to provide initial protection for defensive preparations in the main battle zone. Such was the Israeli purpose in building the Bar Lev Line up to 1973. By checking the enemy advance, the delay force gains time for the rest of the formation, obtains intelligence, confuses the enemy, and identifies the lines of advance that the enemy intends to follow. The troops in this screen, delay zone or covering force, as it is variously described, are required to operate a fine balance. They must hold sufficiently strongly to force an enemy to deploy into battle formation and fight his way forward, yet not so strongly that the delaying troops suffer unacceptably high casualties. For these troops may be required to withdraw into the main battle area, to replenish, and to take part in the major actions ahead. Minefields will be used to assist the covering force in their initial task of hindering and damaging the enemy. Nuisance mining and small minefields will be used to inflict casualties and promote caution in the advancing foe, but the degree of this mine laying will be limited by time, logistics and the amount of mine and engineer resources which the overall commander is prepared to allocate to the delay zone. Some breaching equipment will also be allocated to the forward units. Although their withdrawal routes through the main battle area obstacles will be carefully planned, it can never by guaranteed that those routes will be kept open. Consequently, the delay force needs its own means of clearing routes through enemy scatterable mines placed in their way or for breaking through the minefields in the main battle area.

The defensive zone, in which the decisive battles will be fought by the majority of the defending troops, should be selected as being the terrain offering the greatest advantage to the defender. For many reasons this will rarely be the case, and the commander must alter the ground with artificial obstacles, usually minefields, in his favour. A dilemma now faces the commander and his engineer adviser. Whilst the delay force buy time for them, there is probably a sufficient period for extensive mining to take place. These could be wide, deep minefields denying access through the best tank approaches, or smaller ones offering immediate protection to defended locations. But the design for battle is based on mobile defence, and mining vast tracts of the main defensive area will limit the opportunity for counter-moves by the strong reserves. Thus a balance is struck. Minefields are used to disrupt, delay and divert the already mine-conscious enemy, channelling him into those areas where he can be destroyed. Yet ample room is left between obstacles to allow the defending units to manoeuvre, permitting freedom of tactical action. Within mobile defence, minefields are best viewed as baffles, permitting the battle to ebb and flow, rather than as constraining dams.

The support area, or rear combat zone, tends to be thinly protected by combat troops, but heavily populated with logistic installations. It is here that you will find the supply depots, ammunition or fuel dumps, field hospitals and repair shops. These units are often difficult to conceal or camouflage, are poorly guarded and can only be defended by the unit personnel themselves. They are, however, subject to many threats. It is this area that armoured thrusts try to reach. Alternatively, both helicopter and airborne troops can infiltrate and land more safely in this zone than amidst the well defended forward areas. Equally, saboteurs or special forces could gain successes out of all proportion to their size against these large, sprawling targets. Thus mines can be put to obviously good effect in enhancing the protection of installations and of the area itself. Likely helicopter landing sites or parachute drop zones can be mined. Open areas between units and avenues of approach can be closed with minefields. Fragmentation mines around the perimeters of units will greatly improve immediate defences. Consequently, any force considering a deep penetration raid must be prepared to overcome mines and arm itself with adequate counter-measure equipment.

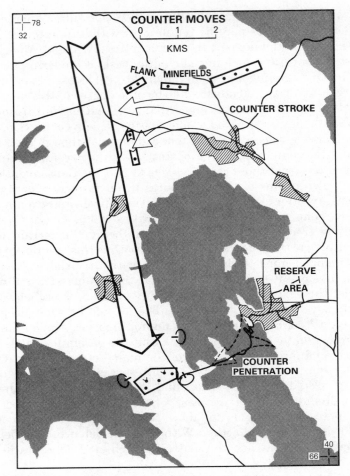

FIG. 3.3. *Counter-moves. Halting an enemy thrust by counter-penetration and destroying the column with a counter-stroke.*

Battle Baffles

Minefields can be usefully categorized into three main types: tactical, protective and phoney. In addition to these, random mining, booby-trapping, placing off-route mines and delivery of scatterable mines can be aggregated into the term nuisance mining. These are NATO descriptions, and other alliances or states may use different terminology. However, they cover all present forms of mine laying and provide a good framework to examine mining concepts further.

Tactical minefields are those planned to have a major effect on the battle. They will be ordered by formation commanders, co-ordinated at a high level, and emplaced by combat engineers. Designed to be very difficult to breach, tactical fields are usually both deep, over 500 metres, and wide, over 1000 metres. Being well fenced and marked an enemy is expected to avoid them, faces delay, becomes

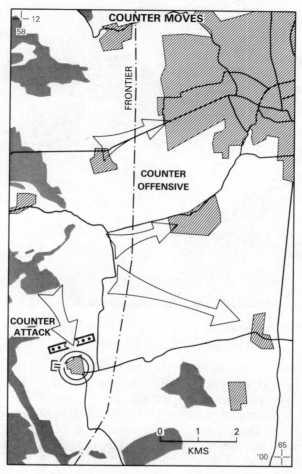

F<small>IG</small>. 3.4. *Counter-moves. A counter-attack on an enemy incursion and a counter-offensive into the aggressor's territory.*

deflected from the original axis of advance and is possibly canalized into a selected fire pocket. If a breaching operation is attempted, this is an excellent opportunity for the defender to inflict heavy casualties, for every minefield should be covered by defensive fire. This can range from artillery to machine gun fire, and could include tank main armament and anti-tank guided weapon engagements.

Such minefields had their origins in the desert campaigns of World War II, where the Afrika Korps and the Eighth Army fought each other through obstacles several miles deep, stretching from the Mediterranean to the Qattara Depression. A more selective use of tactical minefields was demonstrated by the Arab forces in the Sinai, and the Argentinian engineers originally showed a similar understanding of tactical fields on the Falklands.

Within NATO, the development of mechanical mine layers and cross-country,

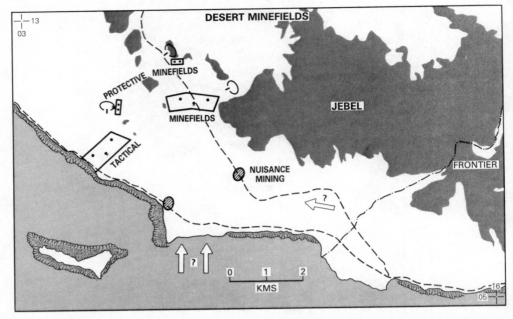

Fig. 3.5. *Desert minefields. Mines can be used in any terrain to hinder mobility.*

load carriers has enabled plans to be adopted which require considerable numbers of minefields to be laid, in depth and over a wide frontage. The skills needed to reconnoitre, plan, lay, record and mark these large fields are exercised frequently. A mine laying task is a complex undertaking, requiring practice and considerable co-ordination between the engineers, the troops in the immediate area where it is sited, the transport unit providing the numerous trucks and the stores depot releasing the vast number of mines and fencing stores. If all this preparation goes well with, hopefully, military precision, then the most dangerous phase can begin. Minefields should be laid at night, to minimize the exposed engineers to observation, although modern surveillance devices make it ever more likely that their activities will be detected. In any case, the engineers are in a very vulnerable position as the fields are normally forward of defended localities, in open countryside, and the inevitable sound of trucks and armoured vehicles could well bring unwelcome attention. Even without enemy interference the activity is inherently dangerous. People are surprised how difficult it is to remain properly orientated in a minefield at night, and this could easily cause a mine laying team to stray on to an armed row of mines with catastrophic results. If co-ordination is vital to the preparations, then control is essential to the execution of a mine laying task. The location of mine rows, access routes and safe lanes all need to be marked, and well-briefed guides are required to escort mine laying and fencing teams about the field.

Protective minefields, on the other hand, tend to be simpler affairs. These are laid to afford close-in protection to a specific locality. Typically, they would be placed in front of a defensive position to prevent it being over-run, and sited so that they could be covered by all the defenders' weapons. Emplaced by hand, they are on a much smaller scale than tactical fields, perhaps 300 metres wide by less than 100 metres deep.

The Bar Lev line on the east bank of the Suez Canal consisted of a string of fortified posts, each surrounded by small minefields. These were examples of protective fields, as were the badly laid, unmarked, mined areas close to the Argentinian positions on East Falkland.

A third type of minefield is the phoney, or dummy. The area is fenced and marked as normal, but contains no live mines. It is an elaborate hoax and the simulation can extend to the emplacement of inert mines within the field or the ripping of empty rows into the surface of the ground. Its value is entirely dependent upon the foe being in a frame of mind where he is fearful of mines. This is mine awareness, a psychological state brought about by a previous, horrifying experience of mines. Phoney minefields can be valuable when mine resources are low and all the required live fields cannot be laid. However, they are of greatest use to the proponent of mobile defence, who wishes to have a rapid but safe route through a defended area. In this case the route is covered by a phoney field, the enemy believes it to be an approach blocked by a minefield and assumes he is secure from assault from that area. Only to be greatly surprised when a counter-stroke force thunders on to him from that very direction.

Originally, nuisance mining referred to such acts as placing mines in the verges of roads, or amongst the rubble of demolished bridges or in farmyards that could be used as vehicle harbour areas. These tactics were mastered by the German troops as they withdrew through Italy, and then through France and Holland. It was this type of random, unmarked mining which found favour with the insurgent and guerrilla groups that proliferated after World War II in places such as Cyprus, Mozambique and Aden forming the eventual basis of the Viet Cong mining campaign against the US forces in Vietman. The development of off-route, scatterable, and remotely delivered mines has now added a new dimension to nuisance mining. Whilst the off-route mine (ORM) is more readily emplaced than the conventional mine, in a greater variety of places (for example, on motorways or to fire down from balconies), it is essentially a pre-placed weapon. However, the scatterable mine (SM) and remotely delivered mine (RDM) are reactive weapons. They can be scattered ahead of, or thrown into the midst of, an advancing or withdrawing enemy. They really do become a nuisance weapon, at the most critical or inconvenient time.

The value of nuisance mining within the total concept for battle is primarily its tendency to promote caution in the minds of the enemy. This mine awareness makes them think twice before attempting to breach a tactical minefield and encourages them to believe that phoney fields are to be avoided. It adds extra stress to a mind already strained by the initial impact of war.

Minefield Siting

Minefield locations should be chosen by the tactical commander, based upon advice from his operations and engineer staffs. The minefields are an integral part of his battle plan and their positioning should not be delegated to engineer or junior commanders, if he is to ensure that they will not interfere with his future manoeuvre options or waste the considerable resources allocated to them. Mined areas will form part of the tactical obstacle plan, which will be designed to prevent or delay an enemy's movement, to divide and disperse his attack, or to shepherd him into positions where he will be particularly vulnerable. These aims will be achieved by a variety of means. Filter obstacles will separate tracked from wheeled vehicles, to inhibit the resupply of vital items to armour, such as ammunition and fuel. Denial obstacles will prevent enemy occupation of specific areas, for example landing sites. Obstacles may also be provided to deceive an enemy into believing he has found a main defensive position. Then there will always be the requirement to provide obstacles rapidly to meet an unexpected threat or support a counter-move.

It is inevitable that on any battlefield where armour has predominance, anti-tank minefields will figure strongly in the obstacle plan. These will be used in conjunction with natural features, their detailed siting being governed by the following considerations:

> *Reinforcement* — slopes, steps, ditches, soft going and other natural restrictions can be used as the basis of an obstacle to be reinforced by a minefield.
> *Bonding* — minefields should link with natural obstacles such as woods, marsh or lakes.
> *Complexity* — the difficulties facing a potential breaching party should be increased by providing combination obstacles, for example, digging an anti-tank ditch within a minefield on the bank of a river or canal.
> *Covered by fire* — as a minimum, any minefield should be covered by indirect fire. Direct fire would be preferable, and the ability to keep the field under constant surveillance should be considered during its design phase.
> *Strength* — the minefield must be capable of achieving its aim. A group of off-route mines along a forest track will defeat a reconnaissance patrol, whilst a strong tactical minefield will be required to close a valley on a main enemy axis.
> *Necessity* — only those minefields needed to support the tactical plan must be provided. They, in turn, must produce the required effect and not inhibit defensive operations.
> *Concealment* — reverse slopes, hedges, buildings can and should be used to conceal minefields from an enemy until he is upon it. This will aid deception, prevent forward planning of a breach and provide a useful element of surprise. Irregularity in a minefield will assist in its concealment and prevent the attacker from deducing the defenders' defensive positions.

Minefield Layout

Each minefield will be constructed to meet a specific purpose. Dimensions, mine density and location will be varied from one field to another to conform with the unique requirement. Nevertheless, there are certain elements of a minefield which should be common to all.

The need to fence and mark minefields is subject to international agreements. NATO nations are required to provide a perimeter fence of at least one strand of wire. This could be plain or barbed, even telephone cable or string will suffice. Some forces prefer to provide a double or triple strand fence on the sides and rear where their own forces could stray on to the mines. At regular intervals along this fence, signs should be hung of a standard design. In the West, these are red triangles with the word MINES picked out in white lettering. If chemical mines were present the letters would be yellow.

Many will be familiar with the term Safe Lane, an expression in common use during World War II. There are, in fact, two types of clear route through a minefield, that can either be left empty during construction or breached as required. The minefield lane is wide enough to allow men or vehicles to traverse the field in single file or column ahead. The minefield gap, on the other hand, is a much wider space permitting a force to cross the minefield in battle formation.

Within the field, mines are sown in rows to achieve a required density. The stopping power of the minefield is dependent upon this density, which should be about one mine per metre of front for reasonable effect. The mines can be mechanically laid or hand placed, on the surface or buried. When a mechanical layer is used the mines are laid one after the other in a line. These lines or rows tend to be widely separated so that a tactical minefield, when viewed from the air, is not the densely packed area of mines that might be expected. A hand-laid, protective field is more in keeping with the common image of a "Garden of Death". The mines in this type are set out in a pattern, which can be paced out or measured out from lengths of knotted string. The mine pattern and method of emplacement are dependent upon national teaching. Minefields can be described as anti-tank, anti-personnel or mixed, the latter being the case when anti-tank mines are laid then protected by anti-personnel (AP) ones. The problem of laying AP mines with mechanically emplaced anti-tank (AT) mines in a big minefield has been overcome imaginitively for British forces, who have the benefit of the Ranger automatic AP mine dispensing system. In the smaller, protective minefields, hand emplacement of the AP mines in a cluster around an AT mine is the norm.

Deep and Devious

A successful defence will rarely be achieved with minefields alone, but they can provide a considerable contribution to the commander's aim when employed properly. This effective use begins with the engineer officer taking an active part in the initial formulation of the tactical plan. In addition to ensuring that there is an unambiguous appreciation of the commander's design for battle on the part of the combat engineers, the sapper officer will, in return, provide balanced advice on the advantages and disadvantages of each type of minefield and proposed location. Inventiveness and imagination are then required to translate the obstacle plan into a series of minefields, sited in depth like a series of baffle plates, to surprise, deceive and hinder an enemy — whilst offering the minimum constraints to defending forces. Beyond this the unexpected must be catered for. It should be anticipated that the carefully contrived obstacle scheme will be overturned, or that the concept of operations will be completely altered once battle is joined. To meet such eventualities, a selection of alternative options will be required, with the manpower and physical resources held in reserve to face these contingencies. What those resources may be will be discussed in succeeding chapters.

4

Anti-tank Mines

The Armoured Threat

THE predominant position of the tank on the battlefield was demonstrated during World War II, a view reinforced in many limited wars since. The present range of main battle tanks (MBT), for example Challenger, Leopard, T-72 and Abrams, reflect an evolutionary development of tanks that were in service in 1945. Although various nations lay different emphasis on the three basic characteristics of armour, namely mobility, firepower and protection, the vehicles produced are remarkably similar. They are heavy machines, tending to be just above or below 50 tons; they mount large calibre guns in centrally placed turrets; they have armour concentrated to protect them from frontal attack. The distribution of armour on a tank is not uniform, the emphasis on the frontal arc being derived from experience in World War II. This revealed that most tanks were engaged and hit from ahead. However, the introduction of both hand-held, light anti-tank weapons (LAW) and a variety of anti-tank guided weapons (ATGW), has generated an increased threat of attack from the side. Thus side armour has had to be increased, probably at the expense of top and rear protection. Skirting plates can also be bolted-on to defend the tracks and running-gear from side attack. The tank designer always has to seek a compromise between mobility and this armoured protection.

A specified road and cross-country speed is required by the military user, and this demands a power-pack of a minimum size to achieve the performance, having taken into account the weight of the vehicle. Adding extra armour reduces the designed performance of the vehicle and degrades its mobility. This is why additional protection for the sides must come from reducing the thickness, hence weight, of armour elsewhere, without affecting the vital frontal portion. These traditional pressures on armour distribution have ensured that the least protected part of an MBT is the base of its flat hull, the belly.

Although the MBT may occupy the dominating position amongst the conventional range of land weapons it can not operate by itself with any certainty of success. The tank is but one of the components of an integrated combat group. Artillery is required to pound the enemy prior to an assault. Engineers must ensure the mobility of the battle formation across any natural or man-made obstacle. The infantry have to protect the armour from ATGW ambush and ultimately clear an enemy defensive position on foot, with gun and grenade. In support of this intense activity are a whole variety of troops: maintenance teams, casualty sections, communications cells and so on. Amongst them will be the

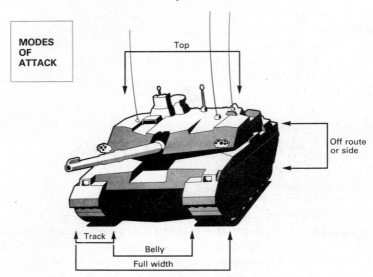

FIG. 4.1. *Modes of attack. The mine can attack tanks from any direction.*

mobile headquarters of units and formations, and if they are fortunate, above them may be close support, ground attack aircraft controlled by air liaison officers. All of these units and detachments have their own transport, thus there are a great number of vehicles on the battlefield, not all of which are armoured. Nevertheless, more and more nations are attempting to armour an increasing selection of these vehicles, and they face exactly the same design constraints as for the MBT. In less powerful machines than the tank, say a wheeled reconnaissance vehicle or tracked ambulance, the amount of armour that can be carried is limited. Equally, the threat may be different and so the armour distribution would alter. For example, an APC must be designed to protect the squad inside from small arms fire and shrapnel from any direction. So it becomes a box of steel or aluminium armour. However, the new range of infantry fighting vehicles (IFV), such as the UK MCV 80 or the US Bradley, are required to keep in close contact with MBT in the advance and attack. They expect to fight it out, face to face, with their counterparts. Hence, IFVs are more heavily armoured than APCs with emphasis once again on the frontal arc. In all of these additional armoured fighting vehicles (AFV), the design compromise leads to the absolute minimum of protection being afforded to the belly, and there is little likelihood that this will alter in the immediate future. Thus the weakest point of every AFV is its belly, which is the area most vulnerable to the mine.

Track-cutting Mines

Traditionally, mines have been pressure activated. Initiation is dependent upon the track or wheel applying sufficient weight to the fuze pressure plate. As MBT grew heavier and track technology improved, the charge content of the mine had to increase to ensure sufficient blast to sever the track and damage the running gear. Whilst this would be a mobility kill against MBT, the volume of explosive used in track attack mines is sufficient to generate critical damage to the vehicle when struck by an APC or truck.

There are reports that Israeli tank crews showed little concern for anti-tank (AT) mines during the Yom Kippur War, having recognized that the mines used by the Arabs were only capable of limited damage to the tracks and road wheels of the Israeli Centurion tanks. The hot gases, molten metal and shrapnel resulting from the explosion were unable to penetrate the solid armour of the hull, and a track repair would soon have the vehicle operational again. This lack of lethality in the AT mine against its primary target can be overcome in several ways. The British Barmine is long and box-like, unlike most AT devices which are circular. This bar construction offers a wider frontage for the mine, increasing the likelihood of contact with a target. It also increases the effect against that target if part of the mine lies to the inner side of the track, below the belly, thereby damaging the crew compartment. Containing more high explosive than most AT mines, the Barmine is not likely to be ignored by any tank crew unfortunate enough to drive over it. Alternatively, just by placing one, round AT mine over another, double the explosive power can be brought to bear on the point of impact. This technique was used frequently in Vietnam against US tanks. Not only does it increase the risk to the vehicle crew, but it also has a devastating effect on mine rollers that may be in use as counter-measures.

However, even the single AT mine is a genuine danger to the plethora of vehicles other than MBT on the battlefield. M113 APCs would be thrown on to their backs or have floors blown open by the force of the Viet Cong mines. Although the crew of the Alvis Scorpion escaped relatively unharmed, when their reconnaissance tank hit an Argentinian plastic mine near Stanley, this vehicle was also blown off its tracks, suffering considerable, external damage. In Aden, British lorries would have the whole cab and engine compartment destroyed by a mine attack on a front wheel. It is evident, that all those vehicles so essential to complement and support the MBT in a combined arms battle remain very vulnerable to the simple, pressure-fuzed AT mine, which has been produced in vast quantities by many nations around the world.

Belly Attack Mines

The vulnerable hull floor is the desirable target area for AT mines, as the greatest risk to the crew then arises from shrapnel, fire or detonation of internally stowed ammunition. To achieve initiation below the tank, the mine could be command detonated on those occasions when the route of the MBT could be predicted, for example in a road ambush. But in the open spaces of a mined area another means must be adopted. The first answer to this requirement was found in the tilt fuze, a thin mast standing proud of a mine, which bent or snapped when the tank's glacis plate grazed against it.

The Soviets developed a unique form of this type of attack against the German Panzers in World War II. By feeding dogs underneath the belly of a tank, the dogs soon began to expect food beneath all tanks. The Russian troops then strapped tilt-fuzed, explosive charges to the dogs' backs and released them towards the

German AFVs. Although the sight of a dog soon began to terrify Panzer crews, such that any stray cur immediately drew the fire of every machine gun in the area, the dog mines were withdrawn after a short while. Apparently, the dogs showed no preference for German over Soviet tanks!

Full Width Attack

Rather than having two types of mine, one fuzed for pressure actuation, another supporting a tilt mast for belly attack, it was long considered desirable to have one mine capable of full width attack (FWA). The need was satisfied when second generation, influence fuzes were developed. These are now available from many sources: Sweden, Italy and France provide them in large cylindrical mines, capable of rapid mechanical laying, and the United Kingdom has designed an FWA fuze for its blast effect Barmine.

The influence fuze may be based upon infrared or magnetic field technology and the FWA mine warhead could be of a shaped or plate charge variety. The significance of the warhead designs being that they are optimized to be armour piercing. Whilst this promises high lethality if the belly is attacked, the effect against the track is not as good as with the high-explosive, blast mine. Although the fuze will react across the whole width of the tank, the real effect of present mines is essentially limited to the belly area. The possible exception being the Barmine fitted with an FWA fuze, since this mine has such a powerful, explosive charge that it will easily slice through a track. Nevertheless, FWA mines of the FFV 028, US M21, MISAR SB MV and GIAT HPD type, are viewed as very cost effective. Although twice as expensive as an ordinary pressure mine, they have been shown to offer 2 or 3 times the probability of engaging a target successfully. Similar cost/benefit assessments indicate that appreciable savings in time and resources can be obtained when using FWA mines instead of pressure mines to achieve the same effect. It can be shown that to obtain the same stopping power as 1000 pressure mines, laid in nearly 4 hours by a platoon operating from three trucks, only 400 FWA mines would be required, which could be laid in under 2 hours from a single lorry. As defence ministries become ever more constrained by tight military budgets, considerations of best effect at lowest cost take on paramount importance. FWA mines come out as a very attractive option in such calculations.

As we shall see later, the influence fuze has to be more intelligent than capable of simply recognizing the arrival of a vehicle overhead. Military requirements often specify that it should be able to differentiate between MBT and APC, and also delay detonation until the mine is below the most vulnerable part of the vehicle. This is generally considered to be the "mid-third" for an MBT. The front part of a tank comprises the glacis armour and the driver's compartment. The centre of an MBT is the turreted fighting compartment, where the radios, crew, ammunition, gun breech and weapon control system are situated. This is the real target for the FWA fuze, although new warheads may soon be developed to ensure effective attack of the engine compartment — the final third of the tank's construction.

Remotely Delivered Mines

The first mines delivered, rather than laid, were the Italian "Thermos Bombs". These were used initially in 1941 against Australian troops in North Africa. Resembling a thermos flask, the mine was dropped from a low flying aircraft and became armed on impact with the ground. Thereafter, they would explode if run-over or disturbed. A novel concept, for several reasons: the mines were air delivered, they were remotely emplaced, they were dropped in rear areas and created considerable psychological stress amongst troops in apparently secure locations. The Russians have used their infamous "Butterfly" mines in a similar fashion against resistance fighters and mountain villagers in Afghanistan. A different type of remote delivery is represented by Standard Industry's Fire Ant. Similar to devices used as "bunker busters" in World War II, this new vehicle is a radio-controlled, six-wheeled carrier for large explosive charges. The unmanned vehicle is directed towards the high-risk target and detonated remotely out to a distance of 1500 metres. An interesting development, if not a true mine in the normally accepted sense.

It is worth considering the terms, remotely delivered mines (RDM) and scatterable mines (SM) for a moment, as they tend to be used incorrectly to describe the same munition. It is true that RDM do scatter when released near the target area, thus all RDM are SM, but the reverse is not true. The Italian mine manufacturers are most accurate in describing their products as scatter mines, because they envisage them being thrown by hand, or scattered from the back of a truck, or dropped from a helicopter dispenser. The TECNOVAR "MATS" mine and MISAR's SB-81 AT mine are designed specifically for such use. Typically, this type of mine is made of non-magnetic material, depends on blast for effect and is fuzed for pressure actuation. It tends to be a sturdy device, of proven technology, that can face rough handling. In other words, the use of SM is normally localized, the mines remain close to the dispenser and their point of impact is visible. This is even true of helicopter delivered mines. Because helicopters are so vulnerable to ground fire, they are hardly ever allowed to fly over ground that is not held by their own troops. Consequently, helicopter SM systems would probably be used for rapid emplacement of an obstacle within a defended area, say in support of a counter-penetration task. Thus SM are short range munitions based upon first generation mine technology.

RDM, as their name suggests, are longer range weapons, whose target area may be completely out of sight of the person dispensing them. Their means of delivery could be howitzer shell, surface to surface rocket or fighter ground attack (FGA) aircraft, and their technology is very much second generation. In fact, RDM systems are dependent upon new fuzes and warheads to be in any way effective. This is simply a matter of size. The internal diameter of a 155-millimetre carrier shell, for example, is much less than that of a conventional anti-tank mine. If a pressure-actuated, blast-effect mine of the size that could fit into a shell was exploded underneath a tank track, there could be no guarantee that the track would split and a mobility kill be achieved. It was evident that a belly attack mine was called for, with an armour-piercing warhead and an intelligent, influence fuze to cause it to detonate at the right point. Once available, these developments had to be miniaturized, then hardened to face the rigours of launching from a field gun or rocket and impacting on any sort of surface from concrete to frozen earth. Not an inconsiderable technical achievement!

Ahead of the field with RDM and SM systems are the American forces. As early as 1977, the M56 mine dispensing pods were fitted to US Army UH-1 helicopters. One helicopter carrying the double pod of 160 mines can lay an SM field some 100 metres by 50 metres in a single sortie. This system is due to be replaced in 1990 by the Volcano dispenser, mounted on the UH-60 Blackhawk aircraft. However, their real lead is most evident in the FASCAM project (Family of Scatterable Mines). Despite the name, the range includes artillery and air delivered RDM, in addition to SM systems. The mines have been designed to achieve a high degree of commonality, using the same standard components where usage and launch conditions permit. The short range members of the family are known as The Ground Emplaced Mine Scattering System (GEMSS) and the Modular Pack Mine System (MOPMS). The same mine is used for both. GEMSS is a trailer mounted dispenser, holding 800 AT mines, that are scattered up to 40 metres from the trailer. MOPMS is an interesting concept, being virtually an automatic mobile minefield. It is a large box containing tubes of mines which can be ejected remotely when required, out to a distance of 35 metres. Thus the pack could be placed in front of a defensive outpost, or to cover a minefield lane, or within a proposed ambush and activated on the approach or an enemy. If none appeared, then MOPMS can be removed, intact, for use elsewhere. This is a rapid, safe and economical development, quite unique amongst mine systems.

The longer range elements of the programme are GATOR and RAAMS (Remote Anti Armor Mine System). The latter is a gun delivered munition, with the mines being ejected from a carrier shell over the target area. The range of delivery is upwards of 15 kilometres from standard 155 millimetre howitzers. The tactical, air delivery system, GATOR, is similar in concept to the cluster bomb. The mines are contained in external canisters which are released from the aircraft, dispensing mines as they fall. All variants of FASCAM have complementary AP versions of the mine which can be scattered alongside, or in lieu of the AT munition.

There is no open information available on Soviet development of RDM systems, however, in view of their past association with, and innovation in, mine warfare, it is unlikely that they will not have some capability in this area. Since both France and West Germany have developed their own SM and RDM, the production of similar systems is well within the technical ability of the Russian armaments industry. Indeed, the German versions may well be a useful indicator of the type of weapons that the Warsaw Pact could field. The AT II mine has been developed for the Bundeswehr to use in four possible ways. A short range, vehicle mounted, dispensing system has been proposed, firing variable tubes of mines out to a range of 20 metres. This would be mounted on a dedicated, tracked chassis and provide an immediate, reactive mine laying capability at brigade level. There is also a helicopter version, the MSM, for mounting on UH-1 aircraft. But their choice for RDM delivery is especially interesting. The mine will be dispensed in rockets from the existing 110-millimetre rocket launcher and the future Multi Launch Rocket System (MLRS). Israeli opinion would also appear to favour rocket delivery, for their Light Artillery Rocket system, LAR 160, is quoted as being capable of accommodating numerous SM. The Soviets have huge numbers of tracked chassis on which they could mount SM dispensers, their helicopter production programme appears to be accelerating, and they have long had multi-barrel rocket launchers in service. Thus the Warsaw Pact could easily introduce any or all of the SM and RDM systems associated with these delivery means. It is of interest to note that the Chinese Army, traditionally inferior in technology to the Soviets, have already fielded an RDM system. This is a rocket based development mounted on a ZIL, six-wheeled chassis. Known as the Type 74 AT mine laying rocket system, it comprises 10 rockets per vehicle with a quoted range of 1500 metres. They have not released information on the mine, or number of mines per rocket, but claim that a battery of four launch vehicles can lay a 400 × 400 metre minefield in one salvo. The Chinese obviously identify the need for such RDM as a counter to the Soviet tank superiority. NATO nations without a similar capability could do worse than to reflect on this Chinese initiative.

Although held on the military inventory of only a few nations, RDM represent a considerable technical achievement and an important milestone in mine warfare. SM and RDM are of unquestionable, tactical significance, providing a new capability on the battelfield. For the first time mines can be viewed as a reactive component of the anti-armour battle, rather than a passive element in the context of counter-mobility. Consequently, it is worth dwelling a little longer on the tactical aspects of these valuable new weapons.

The reasons for adopting mobile defence as the preferred concept have been outlined previously and we have considered the use of pre-planned minefields as elements of the defensive framework. Within an area defended this way, there should be large tracts of territory not denied to the enemy by obstacles, either deliberately to allow the defender to manoeuvre, or as a result of insufficient time or resources to improve the terrain to the defender's advantage. Areas offering unrestricted movement are the natural infiltration and by-pass routes for enemy columns, such as the Soviet OMG (Operational Manoeuvre Group) attempting to penetrate the main defensive zone. Alternatively, an enemy may have sufficient counter-measure equipment to enable him to breach minefields, where they lay on an axis he considers important. Surveillance satellites, information gathering RPVs (Remotely Piloted Vehicles) and real time reconnaissance capability from manned aircraft all enable an attacker to locate and assess minefields on his preferred route, thereby permitting him to plan their breach well in advance. Open access into a defensive area gives rise to the need for a defender to have a rapid mine laying capability, in order to complement his obstacle plan and support counter-moves. If the counter-moves are properly planned, well executed and in sufficient strength, then supplementary obstacles may be unnecessary. But in war, victory can not be guaranteed and any possibility of improving the probability of a successful engagement should be seized. SM and RDM provide that additional opportunity.

The roles for short-range systems include:
(1) Rapid mine laying when time is short.
(2) The imposition of quick response obstacles ahead of an unexpected enemy thrust.

(3) Thickening of other obstacles, such as weak minefields and woods.

(4) Scattering mines in areas unsuitable for mechanical mine laying, eg: water meadows and thick crops.

(5) Closing lanes or gaps in minefields.

These tasks would be undertaken out of contact with the enemy, within the defensive zone. The longer range RDM would normally be used to attack an enemy in depth beyond the main battle line, although the reach of their delivery means does allow them to be employed throughout a formation's area, even across formation boundaries, to deal with a deep enemy penetration. The possible uses for RDM are as follows:

(1) Disruption of enemy movement by mining in front of or amidst their manoeuvre formation.

(2) Separating lead elements from follow-up or logistic forces.

(3) Harassing enemy breaching or bridging operations.

(4) Denial of helicopter landing sites or paratroop drop zones.

(5) Attacking HQ locations, artillery positions or supply dumps.

It is clear from the roles envisaged for both SM and RDM that they are not a replacement for the traditional minefields laid by hand or mechanical means. They are new and complementary weapons, that offer a reactive dimension to the emplacement of obstacles on the battlefield. Indeed, any nation without SM or RDM suffers from a capability gap in its weapon inventory. These mines can be viewed as a reserve of uncommitted obstacles, providing a virtual insurance policy against the unexpected. For the first time, mines can play an active and responsive part in the anti-tank battle.

Off-route Mines

Also known as off-site or horizontally acting mines, the off-route mine (ORM) was originally perceived as a stand-alone, ambush weapon. It could be sited in a side-street or alleyway to fire on to a main road, or placed on the blind side of a bridge or underpass to attack traffic coming through, or beside a forest track to prevent its use. In any situation where a defile constricts movement, and increases the chance of locating a target vehicle, then an ORM has an application. The initial models were based upon anti-tank rockets fired in the side attack mode. During World War II, German troops used the Panzerfaust with a trip-wire fuze and the Soviets developed a proper munition, the trip-wire operated Galitskii Flying Mine, based upon the same principle. More recently both the US M24 and M66 mines used a bazooka rocket and warhead, the difference between them being the fuzing system employed. The former relies upon an electric pressure switch, the latter fires when an infra-red beam is broken. An alternative approach was taken by the French, when GIAT developed the MIACAH mine. This does not utilize a rocket, being a Miznay-Schardin device obtaining its lethality from the plate charge effect. Although later models can be equipped with infrared (IR) sensors, the basic firing mechanism for the MIACAH mine is based upon a break-wire principle. An almost invisible wire is laid across the ambush route, rupturing when the target passes over and initiating the horizontal effect warhead.

All of these mines suffer from the same disadvantages. They tend to be short range weapons, about 40 metres normally, because the length of their break-wires, pressure switches or IR beam cables are limited to this sort of distance. They are time consuming to set-up, as the sensor wires need to be laid out, and the whole system must be concealed and camouflaged. But of most concern is their questionable lethality. This arises from two considerations. Firstly, the fuzes can not compensate for target speed, consequently the warhead may impact outside the important mid-third. Secondly, the warheads are unable to defeat modern side armour. As explained in an earlier section, the sides of MBTs have been up-armoured to match the threat from the increasing numbers of LAW and ATGW available to ground troops. These first generation ORM may not have sufficient penetrative power to overcome the side protection of current AFVs.

An appropriate response to enhanced armour protection has been sought in the LAW area by increasing warhead diameter to promote penetration. This can be utilized in the side attack mine. FFV in Sweden provide a remote wire switch for attachment to their AT4 LAW. The AT4 can then be tied to a tree or lamp post to cover an obvious route and a traversing target will be engaged remotely by a concealed observer. This is a simple system, a more sophisticated assembly is offered by Hunting Engineering of UK under the name Adder, Britain's only venomous snake! Based upon the powerful LAW 80 weapon, Adder provides a firm weapon stand for use on any type of ground, plus a wire control system. However, despite the improved lethality of these warheads, the accuracy of the remote control mine remains low.

The answer to high kill probability from side attack mines, is dependent upon both accuracy and lethality. These two factors are combined to best effect in second generation ORMs, typified by WASPM from the US, the FRG's Panzer Abwehr Richt Mine (PARM) and a British Aerospace development, Lawmine. Using sensors based upon the latest technology, for example fibre optics or millimetre wave radar, the targets can be located, categorized as tracked or wheeled, ranged onto and engaged within their centre-third. The lethality component will be provided through the potency of modern self-forging fragment or shaped charge warheads. Longer ranges are now available from these sensors and attack mechanisms, allowing new roles to be found for modern ORM. Rather than being confined to ambush locations, or the closure of minefield lanes, typical tasks for horizontal effect mines, second generation devices can also be used to dominate open areas or reinforce minefields. Equally, they can be placed high or low, on balconies or below embankments, to engage targets from unexpected directions. In the minefield reinforcement role, they are particularly valuable against counter-mine vehicles mounting rollers, ploughs or flails. These vehicles destroy simple buried or surface laid mines as they advance. Intelligent fuzed, longer range ORM would detect their infiltration through a minefield and attack them from a flank, halting the breach operation in mid-course, and allowing the defenders to bring all available firepower to bear on the immobile attacking force.

Counter Counter-measures

The battle of mine against counter-measures is constantly waged. Even the simplest fuze, the pressure actuation variety, can be modified to defeat detection or clearance devices. Electronic detectors are thwarted by constructing mines entirely of non-magnetic, usually plastic, materials. Against the bangalore torpedo and explosive clearance hose, means of resisting the almost instantaneous pressure of the explosion have been developed. By employing hydraulic or pneumatic delay mechanisms in the fuze, or using tilting cover plates, the sharp, blast overpressure can be absorbed and the mine will only activate on the slower, steady force applied to it by a real target. To prevent hand breachings, some AT mines are fitted with anti-lift devices, a good example being the Cardoen M-19 mine manufactured in Chile. Normally contained within a well, sunk into the base or side walls of the mine, the anti-handling switch turns the normally stable AT mine into an extremely sensitive and dangerous booby-trap. The only way of clearing mines so prepared, is to destroy them *in situ* with small explosive charges.

To overcome the mine roller, the fuze can be separated from the charge. This was an early, improvised approach to the problem and required both time and luck for success. In outline, the explosive part of the mine would be buried some five or so metres on the enemy side of the pressure pad location, both being connected by detonating cord or a similar means of initiation. As the roller activated the pressure fuze the target vehicle itself would be moving over the mine charge and take the force of the explosion, rather than the roller. This layout could only be installed by hand, and a more efficient mechanism was required that would allow mechanical laying. The solution was the double impulse (DI) fuze. Relying upon pressure actuation, the first impulse seen by the fuze would be that from the roller. This would not cause detonation, but would prepare the fuze for the second impulse from the vehicle propelling the roller. As the vehicle track or wheel pressed on the fuze this second time, the mine initiated. An additional, useful feature of the type of fuze is its action against follow-on vehicles when rollers are not in use. When mines are thought to be present, vehicles tend to be driven in the tracks of the vehicle in front. Thus the lead tank would pass over the DI fuzed mine without effect, the next would detonate it. Single impulse (SI) mines can then be used further along the road or in the minefield to deal with the lead vehicle.

The mine plough pushes pressure mines aside and a different type of counter counter-measure is required to defeat it. Whilst mines fitted with anti-lift fuzes could damage the plough, these mines have so far had to be laid by hand. A completely new fuze, optimized for plough attack, and capable of being laid mechanically would be the ideal answer. This has been realized with the production of the anti-disturbance (AD), add-on fuze for the UK Barmine. Similar fuzes, using electronic or mechanical sensors, would cause the mine to detonate either on the arrival of a normal target or if disturbed by a plough. Destruction of ploughs is a desirable objective as they will inevitably be in short supply and either the breach will stop, or be delayed until replacements are obtained. Should the breach continue to be attempted without ploughs, then casualties will be inflicted by uncleared mines, which is exactly why the minefield was there in the first place.

Mine layers

The backbone of any concerted obstacle plan will remain the tactical minefield. But few nations are able or prepared in peace to protect their borders, sensitive areas or important installations with extensive areas of mined ground. When danger threatens, the required minefields must be laid with the greatest possible speed. SM and RDM are expensive, both to purchase and deliver, and are an unlikely choice to meet the requirement for fast, framework minefields. Therefore, continued reliance must be placed on the system of mechanical laying large quantities of patterned AT minefields.

As each nation has developed its own versions of buried or surface laid mines, it has also tended to devise a suitable mine layer to dispense them. Early wheeled versions were towed behind trucks, which carried the mines for laying. If the terrain proved too soft or otherwise difficult for the lorry, then the whole could be

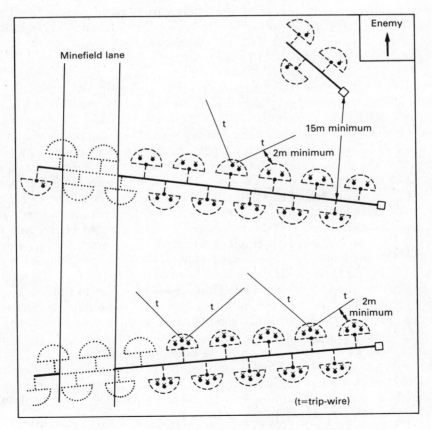

FIG. 4.2. *A typical layout for a hand-laid minefield.*

towed by a bulldozer or APC. These combinations became known as mine laying trains. Cumbersome, slow, difficult to control, susceptible to breakdown and impossible to conceal, mine trains based on equipments such as the UK Mark 3 mine layer, US M57 system, or Soviet PMR-3 mine trailer, were in much need of improvement and replacement.

To complement their advanced, FWA mine, the Swedish FFV company offer the 5821D, a fully automated, wheeled mine layer that can be adapted for towing behind trucks or APCs. The only action to be taken by the crew is removal of the mine safety tab. Using this system, it is claimed that four soldiers can lay 400 mines in less than an hour. Similar figures are not readily available for the latest Soviet mine layer, the GMZ which is a self-contained, armoured and tracked dispenser based on the SA-4 chassis. Probably meant to provide rapid flank protection during an advance it is thought that the GMZ can lay its load of about 200 mines in an hour. However, possibly the best known and most flexible mine laying system in the West at present is the Barmine layer. Optimized for use behind APCs, such as FV432 or the M113, it can also be towed by landrovers, cargo vehicles and high mobility load carriers of the Alvis Stalwart type. Just two men are needed to keep the layer constantly supplied with mines, which can be the standard Barmine or those fitted with DI or add-on FWA and AD fuzes. This allows a complex minefield containing a whole variety of differently fuzed mines, capable of defeating virtually all counter-measures, to be laid quickly from the one type of robust dispenser, whilst the laying team are afforded armoured protection. An experienced crew, supported by a slick resupply organization, would be able to match the FFV laying rate of 400 mines per hour.

Despite the advances at the business end of mine laying, the whole procedure remains a lengthy affair, very demanding in manpower, mechanical handling equipment (MHE) and transport. This is not hard to visualize. Thousands of tons of mines and associated stores are held in base depots in containers or on pallets. They have to be packed on to heavy trucks, trains, ships or aircraft and moved forward into the combat zone. Here they are unloaded into supply areas, where bulky loads are broken down into sizes that conform with transport or MHE available in forward areas. Prior to laying, the mines are moved forward to a unit dump, to be cross-loaded, often by hand, into the APCs or cross-country vehicles which tow the mine layers. Only at this point can the rapid laying rate of the modern layers be exploited to emplace the urgently required minefields.

No doubt in the hope of circumventing some of the logistic difficulties inherent in any mine laying tasks, helicopters have been considered as load carriers. They can certainly be used to deliver underslung loads of mines to remote locations, such as jungle hill tops or forest clearings, however, some nations pursued the possibility further. Great Britain demonstrated a mine chute attached to a Wessex helicopter in the 1960s. The helicopter would follow the lie of the land and AT mines were passed down the chute to land on the surface of the ground. A similar arrangement was used by Russian engineers to lay TMN 46 mines directly from a Hound helicopter. Neither of these have been developed further, not surprisingly in view of the limited capacity of the helicopters concerned and the numbers of sorties required to lay a tactical minefield.

A Formidable Barrier

The diversity and quality of AT mines likely to be met in the combat zone should present a fearful image to AFV crews. The mines could be waiting below their tracks, off to the side behind a bush, or about to fall amongst them from the sky. In the past, MBT crews may have felt relatively safe from the effects of mines and accepted the shock and inconvenience of having a track blown off. No longer can they be so complacent under the threat of lethal attack through the belly or sides of their tank. Taken individually, each type of mine may be countered, but grouped together in tactical minefields the range of AT mines and fuzes form a formidable barrier to any movement or counter-measure. If time permits, and a deliberate breaching operation is attempted, there can be no guarantee that a slowly won gain will not be rapidly negated by clusters of RDM falling on the cleared lanes. These mines now threaten not only the freedom of action of forces in the close contact battle, but also the security of troops in the rear areas, who have become just as susceptible to mine attack. The basis for an anti-armour defence can be effectively provided by the AT mine. However, it is not simply the tank that has to be defeated, mines have been developed to face a variety of threats and we shall assess these in the next chapter.

5

The Alternative Forms

Anti-personnel Mines

THE AP mine was introduced to protect the vast fields of AT mines being sown in World War II from hand breaching parties. As clearance techniques improved, the AP mine developed in phase to maintain the level of deterrence against hand lifting. The mine appeared in new forms with increasing lethality and ever more dangerous means of initiation. It was soon realized that these devices had a much wider application than defending minefields. Despite concerted efforts to increase the scale of mechanization during World War II, the majority of troops still operated on foot. Such soldiers became the target for the AP mine, wherever they marched, bivouacked, patrolled or fought. The weapon took on a fiendish character in the minds of the troops, being a very personal enemy that crippled, maimed and mutilated on an apparently selective and individual basis. AP mines retain these characteristics today. With a few exceptions, the AP device is not designed to kill but wound; usually its objective is to shatter a foot or leg. The casualty is rendered immobile, cannot continue with his task, demands the attention of his immediate fellows and requires rapid evacuation and treatment through the medical support system. This imposes a much greater load on the opposing forces than killing the soldier outright with a more lethal device. These considerations may appear cold and brutal, but combat is exactly that, with mine warfare being one of its most pitiless components.

Yet in the era of mobile forces, the AP mine may seem unnecessary. APCs, IFVs, reconnaissance vehicles and helicopters can be found in abundance to transport soldiers about the battlefield, so it would seem superfluous to have AP weapons with only limited opportunity for employment. Experience shows that this is clearly not the case. For low intensity operations and jungle warfare, their utility is obvious. Against human wave tactics, evident in the war between Iran and Iraq, they provide a valuable source of close protection. They were also a factor in British operations on the Falkland Islands, where limitations on transport forced the troops to advance and assault on foot. Even within the potential battle scenario envisaged for war in Europe, the requirements for AP mines remain. For example, they encourage caution and mine awareness amongst an enemy, when included in mining tasks ahead of the main battle area. Equally, within AT minefields they are needed to deter sapper recce patrols, to threaten hand breaching parties, and to endanger the surviving crews of AFVs that have been stopped by the AT mines. The AP mine can also be used to deny helicopter landing sites, to guard covered approaches to positions, and to bolster

35

protective minefields. They continue to be valuable in the latter role, as a defended location can only be cleared properly by troops assaulting through every trench and bunker on foot. In other words, to be effective, infantry must leave the protection of their APC or IFV and fight through a position to guarantee it has been taken. When they debus to do this, the assault troops become vulnerable to the AP mine, even though most other defending weapons may have been silenced by artillery or enemy suppressive fire. In this respect, mines provide a very survivable defensive weapon.

As with the anti-armour mine, the most common form of AP device is that based upon the pressure fuze. It may be of interest to note here that the only recorded anti-camel mine, one initially produced in Persia (Iran), also depends upon pressure as the form of initiation. The pressure required to detonate this mine is too great for the device to be designated an AP mine although it can be used to good effect as an anti-vehicle mine. The very first AP mines were simple, hinged box affairs, made of wood, containing an explosive charge. The weight of a man would press the cover of the box down on to a restraining pin, releasing a striker to detonate the mine. Such devices were used by the Argentinians on the Falklands and continue to be manufactured in some places, in Israel it is known as the No. 4 mine. Easy to detect, with detector or prodder, the box mine gave way to smaller mines with minimum metal content, but sufficient explosive to severely damage the foot or lower leg. Initially made of bakelite or resin these mines were easy to carry, lay and conceal; extremely difficult to detect and clear. Examples of these are the Canadian Elsie and American M14 mines. As plastics technology improved, the new techniques were absorbed into the development of non-magnetic AP mines. PRB, a Belgian firm, offers two mines made in moulded plastic the M35 and the M409. The former has a very low probability of sympathetic detonation, being designed for laying in close combination with AT mines in mixed minefields. The disc shaped M409 on the other hand, has an extremely sensitive fuze, that can cause the mine to detonate under the pressure of a mine prodder, a fearful prospect for breaching parties. Most other nations produce plastic AP mines now to benefit from their cheapness in mass production and virtual non-detectability. The Spanish P4B, South African RDX, Bofors LI-11 or Misar SB 33 mines typify the modern, pressure actuated AP mine.

Whilst the pressure device depends upon actual contact and attacks the individual, a requirement was recognized for a weapon that both dominates an area and threatens more than one target. The German S mine proved to be a frightening solution. Probably the most feared and respected device encountered by Allied troops in World War II, the S mine was activated by a trip-wire or pressure on one of its three prongs. It formed the model for many future jumping, or bounding, mines as they are called. The M16 and M26 mines used by the US forces are of this type, comprising an ejection charge and a shrapnel warhead. Normally buried to the shoulder of the casing, with the fuze just proud of the surface, the cylindrical mine is shot into the air by the ejection charge, where it explodes scattering splinters in all directions. Variations on this theme can be found, all of them lethal rather than damaging, in close proximity to the mine. Israel Military Industries produce the MI2AI mine, which has a casing of steel balls to act as projectiles, whilst PRB's NR442 bounding mine uses pre-notched wire to produce uniform circular dispersion of the 2,500 wire splinters. A unique weapon of this kind is Valsella's erecting mine, the VS-ER-83. As the name suggests, the mine is not propelled into the air like a true jumping mine, but lies horizontally, hinged to a picket. This allows it to be laid on the surface of the ground, along the top of a wall or fence, or below the lip of a window sill or ditch. Activated by trip-wire or initiated by a remoted, electrical exploder the mine is thrust into a vertical position, where it detonates. Covering a full 360 degrees (6400 mils), out to a lethal radius of 50 metres, the mine projects 1600 steel balls quite capable of penetrating and damaging unarmoured vehicles. All of these jumping and erecting mines need to be emplaced by well trained personnel, and to render them safe after laying is extremely hazardous. They can be used in all situations where other AP mines may be employed, however, with some splinters reaching out to 200 metres, their radius of action requires them to be placed in locations that can not endanger friendly troops.

Nevertheless, the multi-directional nature of the bounding mine can be an unwelcome threat to the very soldiers it is meant to protect. To overcome this problem, a safer, directional fragmentation mine was designed to provide close defence and also act as a new form of ambush weapon. Known in the West as the Claymore mine, it has been manufactured in several forms. In Chile, the Cardoen company produce the M18 mine, based upon the original American version, whilst FFV in Sweden have developed their own area denial mine, the 013. The mine consists of a sheet of high explosive faced with a layer of steel pellets. It can be fired remotely by detonators, individually or in banks of several devices, or fitted with trip-wire initiators. On detonation, the pellets are propelled into a 60 degree arc, capable of killing at 100 metres and wounding at 250 metres. Offering rapid and devastating firepower, directional mines are useful in denying helicopter landing sites or parachute drop zones, defending open areas such as airfields, defeating mass infantry attack and in reinforcing ambush locations. Easily carried and providing exceptional effects for their size, these mines are considered to be excellent weapons for close protection on patrol or in defensive locations. A well publicized use for a similar type of mine was on the Inner German Border. The SM70, or RATTE, mine has been placed by the East German authorities along their side of the barrier obstacles, which they had installed, as an additional deterrent to those wishing to cross to the West. Lethal out to a range of 30 metres, the cone shaped, RATTE mine was usually fired by a sprung, micro-switch initiator attached to the border fence. Arranged in clusters of 3, one each at knee, waist and head height, they have been responsible for the deaths of several would-be escapees since the mines were initially installed in 1971. For a reason never explained, the East Germans began to remove many of the mines during early 1984, although it has been reported that some were since replaced by an improved model, the SM701.

Just as AT mines can be scattered or remotely delivered, so can the AP mine. The Italian manufacturers Misar, Tecnovar and Valsella all produce plastic devices for dispensing by hand, from vehicles or from below helicopters. They can be used alone to deny areas to soldiers on foot, or concurrently with plastic AT mines. The Soviet PFM1 mine is the only Eastern Bloc AP SM, about which information is readily available. It has been called the Butterfly mine or the

Green Parrot, as a result of its winged body and green colouring, although it can be found in snow or desert colours. The winged shape acts as a simple aerofoil when it is dropped from helicopters or fixed-wing aircraft and also excites curiosity amongst those who find it on the ground, since the device does not look like a mine, but an interesting toy. Many of the casualties amongst the Afghan people have arisen out of the temptation for them to handle the mines when they find them. Unknown to the tribesmen the pressure fuze works on a cumulative principle. Each time a small pressure is applied to the polythene body it contributes to the total force seen by the fuze until the limit, about 5 kilograms, is reached, at which point it explodes. With only 40 grammes of liquid explosive as the charge, the PFM1, sometimes designated the PMZ, rarely kills outright but maims and mutilates, usually leading to amputation. The UK scatterable AP mine is known as Ranger. This is a cylindrical, pressure mine supplied in tubes of 18. Four of these tubes form a magazine module. The magazines are mounted in a standard rack which can hold up to 18 of them at a time. Thus a fully charged rack of 1296 mines can be fired in a ripple effect out to a distance of some 100 metres in one minute. Within the British Army the Ranger discharger is normally mounted on the roof of an AFV 432 and fires AP mines into the tactical fields sown by the Barmine layer. However, the Ranger system has base adaptors which allow it to be fitted on to landrovers, cargo vehicles and Combat Support Boat. This latter configuration allows mining to take place in areas that may be otherwise difficult to reach, such as the piers and abutments of demolished bridges, on canal or river banks and on beaches.

Remotely delivered AP mines are probably the exclusive possession of the United States. The GATOR air delivered mine system comprises both AT and AP mines in free fall containers. The mines are similar in appearance and ballistically matched to ensure close protective grouping on the ground. These interdiction minefields would be placed out beyond the range of field or rocket artillery. For closer targets ADAM would be used. This is the howitzer delivered Area Denial Artillery Munition. Over 30 of these mines can be dispensed from a single 155 millimetre carrier shell. As the mine impacts, tripline sensors are deployed from the mine body, sensitive to the slightest disturbance. If triggered, the mine ejects a shrapnel warhead to detonate at head height. The mine dispersion, sensor reach and warhead range all contribute to this munition being a unique and very effective area denial weapon.

Airfield and Area Denial Munitions

Despite the acclaimed success of Israel's pre-emptive strike against Arab airfields in the Six Day War, all nations continue to rely upon high-performance aircraft requiring major runways for take-off and landing. Those few powers possessing a vertical, or short take-off and landing (VSTOL) capability within their air forces have only invested in a limited number of VSTOL aircraft. For conventional aircraft, a token of protection has been afforded on some airfields by the construction of hardened shelters. Despite this, the airfields continue to need considerable lengths of vulnerable runway to meet their operational commitments. Accordingly, runways have become a prime target.

A variety of air delivered weapons are now available to attack roads, runways and taxiways to render them unusable through cratering. The present counter to this threat is to train airfield damage repair (ADR) teams, capable of repairing strips of concrete surface such that air operations can continue. However, to undertake these repairs the ADR units must first make a reconnaissance of all areas that may be suitable for aircraft take-off. This damage assessment exercise permits the selection of a minimum operating strip that allows air operations to continue, whilst requiring the least number of craters to be repaired. The repairs are effected by an ADR troop equipped with numerous items of heavy plant, including excavators, bulldozers and tipper trucks.

Evidently, it is unacceptable to the attacker to penetrate air defences, risk the loss of aircraft, expend costly munitions and then have the results of those efforts overcome in only a few hours. The JP 233 airfield attack system was developed to prevent this. Consisting of the SG357 cratering bomb and HB 876 area denial mine, the system is designed to disable runways or other essential operating surfaces and inhibit their repair for the maximum possible time. The HB 876 munition is dispensed from a container pod suspended below Tornado. Retarded by parachute, the mines land close to the craters produced by SG 357 and are placed in the correct attack position by a self-righting, spring device. The warhead consists of a Miznay-Schardin plate charge and a fragmentation casing, which explodes over a 360 degree arc. The plate is quite capable of penetrating the blade of a clearance dozer and damaging the engine, whilst the canister fragments threaten reconnaissance and repair parties, light vehicles, bomb disposal teams and parked or taxiing aircraft. Thus, in one low-level attack, an airfield can have its runways destroyed and the surrounding areas denied to those on foot and in vehicles, inhibiting all efforts to restore the airfield to operational status. JP 233 was developed in the United Kingdom primarily as an airfield attack system, although it can be used against other targets such as marshalling yards, supply depots and vehicle concentrations.

The West German approach to air delivered, area denial mines has been different. Their multi-purpose weapon, MW-1, carried on Tornado and F-4 Phantom has been prepared with a range of sub-munitions to meet a variety of targets and situations. Within the 2 broad categories of battlefield interdiction and airfield denial, targets can be selected for attack by a suitable mix of shaped charge bomblet (KB44), runway cratering bomb (STABO), anti-shelter munition (ASW) and three types of mine.

MIFF is the abbreviation for Mine Flack Flack, a free-fall AT mine. The role envisaged for this mine is in interdiction tasks along likely deployment routes or against holding areas to hinder the movement of reserve or second echelon forces. The cylindrical MIFF has a double warhead, which allows it to fire from either end. Sprung steel bands on the curved surface ensure that it always sits on one of these flat ends and a passive sensor, thought to be acoustically tuned to engine vibration, gives the mine a full width capability.

The parachute retarded MUSA (Multi Splinter Active) and MUSPA (Multi Splinter Passive) mines are for low level attack of airfields. Both have the same steel ball fragmentation warhead, with a probable effective range of 100 metres. MUSA has a time delay fuze and its detonation point is unpredictable, making even cautious movement through a mined area extremely hazardous. MUSPA, however, has a passive influence fuze which reacts to taxiing aircraft, runway repair equipment and reconnaissance vehicles. The problems of breaching or clearing an area mined by a mix of these weapons are great indeed and ADR units will have their work severely hampered when these, or similar, area denial mines are in evidence.

Anti-helicopter Mines

Although every attempt should be made to restrict helicopter operations to airspace over ground held by friendly forces, there are specific operations which require helicopters to enter enemy territory or areas where hostile air defence systems may be operating. Typically, transport helicopters may have to infiltrate assault troops into position, or attack helicopters may be needed to support a counter-stroke. Thus, a range of options exist for the use of mines against helicopters. So far, attention has concentrated on defeating utility helicopters, and the troops disembarking from them, at landing sites. These are easier targets, and more predictable, than the Lynx TOW and Hind type ATGW helicopters. Flying low to reach fire positions, concealed behind tree lines or buildings, such aircraft can engage targets several kilometres distant. They survive through speed, concealment and a degree of armoured protection. Consequently, they are a difficult target themselves, particularly for anti-helicopter mines. If their fire positions could be predicted, or flight paths detected, then mines could be pre-placed or remotely delivered to deal with them. However, this capability must wait for the future, and current effort will continue to be directed towards the troop carrying helicopter.

Improvisation has been the history of anti-helicopter mines to this point. The use of DH-10 directional fragmentation mines by the Viet Cong to attack US helicopters has been referred to in an earlier chapter. Any potential landing area can be covered in an interlocking fashion by devices of this type, to be remotely detonated when most of the troops have deplaned, catching them in an instantaneous, lethal cross fire. Jumping mines are useful in this role too. Placed in a random fashion through an open area, with trip-wire fuzes, they can easily catch a careless foot. Soldiers are trained to disembark quickly from helicopters and move rapidly away from the aircraft. In their haste, they tend not to be looking for the narrow trip-wires that will fire the fragmentation warhead to a height where it will attack both personnel and helicopter alike. With few exceptions, helicopters have thin skins of light aluminium and perspex, offering no protection to the crew and avionics against the high velocity fragments. Even more rudimentary arrangements can endanger the helicopter as a result of this vulnerability. For example, staked grenades, with trip-wires attached to their safety pins, are an expedient replacement for bounding mines.

However, no specific anti-helicopter mine yet exists. This is surprising as acoustic or heat seeking sensors could be used to orientate fragmentation or plate charge warheads towards hovering helicopters, and all within the bounds of present technology. Undoubtedly such mines are needed, and may be under active development at the moment. They will provide an extra element of protection against heliborne landings and a deterrent to such operations, particularly in rear areas where combat troops are few and widely dispersed.

River Mines

River lines and canals have long been favoured as the natural obstacle to form the basis of a defensive plan. Equally, nations with coastlines have sought to protect their territory in time of war by defeating any incursion on the beaches. Traditionally, naval mines have been used in the defence of coastal waters to attack shipping and landing craft, but now shallow water mines are available for use against amphibious vehicles and small craft. Valsella's VS-RM-30 is typical of these, being influence fuzed with a 30-kilogram high-explosive charge. It is usually placed in position by frogmen, who anchor it to the bottom at a depth no greater than 10 metres. To prevent interference with underwater defences, there are AP mines designed to protect against underwater swimmers. The EPR/6 from Tecnovar achieves this by detonating at a pre-set time, after being laid from the back of the boat. Obviously, most of these devices can be used in rivers and canals too, and even greater flexibility is shown by the Tecnovar EPR/2-5 underwater mine. This can be dropped from light aircraft, helicopters or surface vessels into 40 metres of water as a counter to frogmen or coupled to a simple magnetic device to act as a timed limpet mine. Despite such advances in specialist waterproof devices, land mines have also been adapted for use below water, the US M15 with metal stabilizers is an example, and the Dutch, appropriately, produce a special purpose river mine and fuze assembly, which they call Mirjam. As long as potential enemies maintain marine forces, floating bridges or amphibious vehicles there will continue to be an operational requirement for shallow water mines. Although they can be more dificult to lay than the conventional land mine, they are much less vulnerable to detection and counter-measures. River mines add an extra dimension to the mine threat, attacking an enemy during that vulnerable period when he is attempting to cross a water obstacle or storm ashore, and achieving surprise since their presence is often not expected. They can never be fully replaced by simply mining water meadows or beaches with standard mines, and could usefully be considered for much wider employment than appears to be the case at present.

Chemical Mines

There is little information available on chemical weapons in general, and even less on mines containing chemical agents. However, it is known that the use of chemical mines will be strictly controlled, after their release has been authorized at the highest level of government. Yet they do represent a very cost effective defensive barrier. For example: each mine poses a lethal threat to anyone attempting to neutralize the device; measures normally adopted in breaching, such as flails and explosive hoses, merely release the chemical contamination to attack those doing the breaching; and, collectively, within a minefield they provide a true area denial weapon. Nevertheless, political constraints on chemical mines and the practical difficulties of laying them in full protective clothing prevent their use from becoming widespread. This is a situation that is likely to prevail within NATO, but elsewhere nations with vulnerable borders may recognize the efficiency of these mines in protecting such frontiers. They are simple devices and purely defensive, offering no threat to a potential foe unless borders are crossed and territory violated. Their simplicity is illustrated by the US chemical mine M1, which is little more than a one gallon can filled with mustard gas. It is buried just below the surface and its contents are released by a cutting charge of detonating cord or plastic explosive. Alternatively, almost any AT mine casing could be adapted to accept chemical agent and a bursting charge. This is the origin of the M23 nerve agent mine, which shares a common case with the M15, pressure actuated AT mine. Naturally, there will be concern over the depositing of dangerous chemicals in the ground, even if they are there to protect the nation. Such objections are mostly overcome with the development of binary agents. These are compounds which are individually harmless, but form a lethal agent when combined. Within a mine, the binary compounds can be easily separated by a membrane, rupturing on detonation and allowing combination to take place only when meant to do so. It will be interesting to note any future proliferation of chemical mines, either in the Middle East, resulting from the reported employment of chemicals in the war between Iran and Iraq, or amongst NATO nations, arising from recent high-level military comment that chemical weapons should be enhanced in quality and quantity to strengthen their deterrent value to the West.

Atomic Demolition Munitions

The reader will not be surprised to know that even less information is released on atomic mines than on chemical ones. Yet their utility is just as apparent. For a small mass, the atomic mine has enormous, explosive energy and this would be exploited in its tasks. Typically, the mine would be positioned, in great secrecy, during a period of tension, once political release had been agreed. Likely targets would be those requiring an otherwise unrealistic amount of high explosive, such as mass reinforced concrete bridges or viaducts, railway tunnels, dams, mountain pass roads, valley floors or major road and rail junctions. Unlike devices we have reviewed so far, the nuclear demolition mine is not target responsive. It is emplaced and then initiated in all probability by a delay mechanism. Thus, it should not be a weapon that combat engineers or other troops meet on the battlefield other than to face the after-effects of its detonation. Nevertheless, they could be required to recommend suitable targets, guard the installation party or assist in emplacing the atomic mine and should be prepared for the existence of such devices, and their use, in any major conflict.

Improvised Explosive Devices

At quite the other end of the scale from tactical nuclear munitions, are improvised explosive devices (IED), which cover booby-traps, terrorist bombs, insurgent culvert mines and unorthodox employment of standard munitions. Although it may be considered normal to meet these devices during low intensity and anti-terrorist operations, in fact they tend to be encountered at all levels of conflict. Throughout World War II various Resistance groups resorted to terrorist bombing, and conventional forces prepared mines from shells, drums of petrol or napalm (called Fougasse), explosive, even torpedo warheads. Booby-traps have been a danger in wars and counter-insurgency campaigns, often formed from AP or AT mines, and British troops in Ulster have been a frequent target for terrorist land mines. Thus, all troops in all theatres should expect to meet IED. However, the complexity of some modern terrorist devices calls for specialist expertise to neutralize them safely, and most nations have highly trained disposal teams in their police and military forces to deal with such threats.

The use of mines as booby-traps is a more common skill, which all soldiers should possess, if only to heighten their awareness of the danger to them from similar devices. Booby-traps are employed in a comparable way to nuisance mining. They are hidden where enemy troops are most likely to fall foul of them, perhaps in buildings that could be used for shelter or possibly left behind in evacuated positions. Their purpose is to instil fear and caution in the opposing forces, thereby inhibiting freedom of action and reducing the tempo of operations. Sensitive, pressure fuzed AP and trip-wire fragmentation mines are easily incorporated into booby traps. A loose tread on a flight of stairs can conceal a simple pressure mine, whilst a trip-wire stretched behind a door could release a bounding shrapnel mine as the door is opened. The AT mine can also be used to devastating effect in a booby-trap. Those with tilt fuzes, such as the UK Mark 7 mine, can be placed in a hole in the floor boards behind a door. When the door is swung open, it bends the tilt fuze and most of the house will disappear in the resulting explosion. Mines fitted with anti-handling devices can be similarly used, and those which rely upon an anti-lift pull-switch are particularly effective in booby-trapping windows. In this type of trap, the mine is secured firmly to a wall or floor beside the window. The anti-handling pull fuze is screwed into the well on the side or bottom of the mine and its anchor wire nailed to the moving part of the window. Opening the window has the same deadly effect as lifting the mine under normal conditions.

Just as mines are used in booby-traps, other munitions have served as mines. It only requires a little inventiveness to place a 500 kilogram bomb in an upright position below a bridge, such that its nose fuze stands slightly proud of the road surface, to turn it into a lethal land mine. This is exactly what the Japanese did in the Pacific Theatre. Artillery shells and torpedo warheads were used in a similar fashion, when mines were unavailable, and on the Falklands the Argentinian minefields were protected by booby-trapped grenades. The Viet Cong were just as imaginative in constructing home-made mines. Using explosive from whatever source they could obtain it, such as unexploded bombs or shells, they would pack it into empty 105-millimetre cartridge cases, 5-gallon jerricans, abandoned ammunition cases or roughly moulded cement pots for emplacement in roads, concealed below dead snakes or buffalo dung, as anti-vehicle mines. AP mines would be made from coconut husks or bamboo, and hung in trees to attack their targets from above. Terrorists everywhere have found a use for mines. When South African security police in the Ingwavuma district of mountainous northern Natal uncovered the largest arms cache ever found within their borders, they reported a large proportion of the hoard to be land mines and explosives. The utility of such mines to anti-government forces was amply demonstrated in early 1985 by separatist terrorists in Sri Lanka. Their unfortunate victim was the Commander of the Sri Lankan Army's Northern Command, who was killed whilst his four escorts were badly wounded when their vehicle hit a land mine. The IRA have been equally lethal in their mining of country roads in Northern Ireland. Their mines have inevitably been remotely controlled devices contained in road side milk churns, or jammed into culverts or concealed in hedges. Security forces there have become experienced in recognizing potential ambush sites, locating control wires or firing points and thinking through the double and triple traps set by the lurking terrorist. These have been hard-earned skills, but essential to successful containment of the merciless violence, and valuable elsewhere too. For example, during their occupation of the Falklands, the Argentinians had mined the Stanley to Darwin road near Mount Harriet. When the British Sappers found the command wire and eventually excavated the area, they discovered two aerial bombs, topped by both TNT explosive and AT mines with AP fuzes fitted (Spanish C3B mines, with a 5 kilogram actuation pressure). A hazardous episode, repeated in the clearance of a further land mine on the airport road at the narrow Canache isthmus, the success of which depended on skills and experience acquired in the dangerous border areas of Ulster.

Mines are sinister enough weapons when used in their normal role, they can become fiendish if modified into booby-traps. Other munitions can be adapted to become mines, and these tend to be highly effective, often producing extensive overkill against their selected target. Whilst mines are produced in great numbers their issue is restricted to, and strictly controlled within, official military forces. Terrorists, insurgents and guerrillas would generally find it difficult to lay their hands on manufactured mines, unless they were receiving support from an outside power. Thus, IEDs form an important element in the armoury of any irregular force. Conventional troops, therefore, need to be aware of what form these might take. They should also be prepared to improvise for themselves, as supply lines can not always be guaranteed, and soldiers may have to make the best of whatever is to hand. In peacetime, training in the local manufacture of lethal devices and counters to them is difficult and, regrettably, often forgotten. Fortunately, training with standard mines is not so neglected.

Training Mines

The dangerous nature of mines gave rise to the production of inert, training models, which were used for precise practice on the arming and disarming drills associated with the live versions. Initially, the training mine was made from the same case and material as the operational device, only filled with a harmless substance such as sand or beeswax. As the demand for mines grew and the size of minefields increased, it became necessary to produce training mines in ever larger numbers to simulate the mechanical laying drills involved. To keep costs down, rough copies of mines were made from cheap materials, a concrete version of the UK Mark 7 mine was produced, for example. These cheap models were used with mine layers to lay tactical minefields on exercises, allowing all elements of a unit to be practised in their specific responsibilities: recce officers, in siting and laying-out the minefield; commanders and staff, in planning and controlling the whole operation; junior officers and NCOs, in detailed supervision of the tasks; drivers, plant operators and sappers, in their individual duties. To further minimize the costs of training, and to overcome the problem of expending unproductive time in lifting all the laid training mines, some nations have developed bio-degradable mines. The Ranger AP system fires peat replicas and the British Army also uses cardboard Barmines filled with sand, to lay large minefields during manoeuvres. All of these mines can then be left *in situ* after the exercise without harm to the environment. In addition to both the precise and the less accurate training models, a further version was required. This third practice mine was needed to demonstrate the activation of a mine, either by mishandling or through target contact. The latter requirement is important for several reasons: to test that the laying drills were carried out correctly, to promote confidence in the effectiveness of mines and to induce mine awareness in all troops during training. Traditionally, the indication of initiation has been through the mine generating a puff of smoke, hence the term puff mine. The Canadian Elsie AP mine uses this technique, as does the MILTRA version of the Soviet TMN 46 AT mine. The training model of the MIACAH French ORM, has a different mechanism to indicate a successful engagement. This practice mine fires a sponge, impregnated with chalk, to strike the side of a crossing target vehicle.

As second generation mines became more complex with the introduction of influence fuzes, so did their training version equivalents. Typical is the GIAT XF1A model of their HPD mine, an FWA practice device that fires red smoke for 30 seconds when an AFV is detected. Similar replicas will be needed for SM systems. However, under peacetime conditions RDM delivery would not normally be permissible outside of isolated training areas. The use of RDM will need to be simulated for exercises in some way other than by depositing puff mines. Indeed, minefield simulation is required to overcome a variety of difficulties presently experienced in mine warfare training. The first is the high cost of FWA practice mines, which contain the operational influence fuze, and can not be afforded in sufficiently large numbers to represent the full stopping power of a tactical minefield. Next is the need to illustrate the effect of new ORM, with extended range and improved sensors. The characteristics of these ORM warheads can not be adequately represented by missiles such as the MIACAH sponge and truly representative projectiles would be unacceptable on safety grounds. Finally, there is the requirement to make the target accept the results of a mine encounter. AFV crews involved in an exercise are generally reluctant to acknowledge that their vehicle has been disabled by a mine and will tend to ignore smoke mines, or not even know that they have been hit by a MIACAH sponge, unless strict umpiring is in operation. A more positive and instantly recognizable form of simulation is required. One system that has potential for minefield simulation is the laser weapon effect simulator. An example of this is that offered by Weston Simfire, consisting of a variety of direct fire, laser projectors that are detected by receivers mounted on a vehicle. Once a hit is recorded, coloured smoke and flashing lights are triggered on the target vehicle. Nobody, crew, attacker or umpire, is then in any doubt that a successful engagement has taken place. This technology could be applied to minefield simulation by positioning laser sources along the rows of emplaced training mines.

Vehicles equipped with laser detectors that cut these beams will generate the smoke and light alarms, indicating a vehicle kill. A series of acoustic sensors, triggering ground alarms, could provide an alternative mine effects simulator. Surprisingly, at the time of writing, the requirement for a minefield simulation system has not been adequately met. This is a major deficiency in the availability of training resources and can only diminish realism on exercises. Unless the stopping power of minefields is demonstrated to manoeuvre forces during peacetime training, they will have a hard lesson to learn in war.

Diverse Dangers

These last two chapters have illustrated the wide range of mine types, and the numerous forms that each type can take. Different nations can manufacture mines of the same category, producing similar effects, yet totally different in construction. A bewildering selection of devices confronts any soldier attempting to prepare himself to counter them. Indeed there is no known international and comprehensive catalogue of mines, probably because some mines still in service were fabricated as far back as World War II, some are classified and kept secret on account of their sophisticated sensing systems, some nations do not publicize their military equipment, and new mines are constantly being developed. Thus a researcher would never be sure that his work was complete. The only general preparation a combat engineer can make for counter-mine warfare is to study how mines are used and understand the technical principles behind their construction. Then, once a specific nation is identified as a potential enemy, familiarization with their particular mines can be pursued. This, of course, is the ideal when time and information allow. If the enemy is secretive by nature, as the Warsaw Pact states seem to be, information on their devices can be hard to come by. If the enemy are irregular forces, they may well make their own mines from IEDS or buy them from unknown sources. And if, as is most likely, the enemy is an unexpected opponent, there will be little chance to become familiar with his mines prior to hostilities and the sapper must confront the mines for the first time in combat. This was the situation facing Royal Engineers of the Falklands Task Force, who had little idea of the types of mine in use by the Argentinians, and few details about those they knew of. To acquire the necessary information, young sappers had to infiltrate booby-trapped minefields and recover examples of the live mines. They achieved this through courage, determination and a thorough grounding in the basic principles of mine construction and operation. We shall look at these essential mine components in the next chapter.

6

Mine Technology

Design Principles

Safety

A MINE is a mechanism which has been optimized to kill or injure. It contains high explosive, a sensitive detonator and a keen sensing component. Sometimes it is configured to fire if tampered with. Yet this volatile, lethal device has to be mass produced, stored in large numbers, carried in any variety of transport from long range aircraft to armoured vehicles, handled by MHE and men, dropped (sometimes deliberately, often misadvertently), laid remotely, mechanically, or by hand, armed, neutralized and lifted. And all of this must be done safely. The safety requirements for mines are undoubtedly demanding, but have to be satisfied, since no nation could contemplate the production or purchase of mines likely to deteriorate in storage to an extent where they become unstable, or which detonated whilst being handled or transported. Obviously, mines that earned a reputation for being unpredictable and dangerous to arm or lay, would soon produce morale and discipline problems amongst troops expected to use them. For these reasons safety panels and quality assurance boards specify high standards for the mine designer to meet. Typically, one requirement might be the probability of accidental firing being as low as one in one million. These levels of security have been met in the past and recent developments in delayed arming and remote control will ensure that soldiers will have the same confidence in future generations of mines. To validate the design, extensive trials are undertaken on development, prototype or pre-production models. These trials are normally carried out under the supervision of representatives from the munitions safety panel and examine the response of the mine to all those environmental conditions that it is likely to encounter during its service life. For example: it will be stored in hot and cold chambers to simulate desert and arctic weather, it will be dropped, jolted and vibrated as if it were being transported on a ship, below a helicopter or in a truck, and it will be subjected to blast and electro-magnetic pulse (EMP) effects to measure its resistance to conventional and nuclear explosions. At the production point, modern test techniques, such as X-ray photography, ensure that quality is maintained and samples of each manufactured batch are extracted to face proof. This is a test to destruction to confirm that the mass produced mine reacts as it should to its potential target. In-service proof is a series of similar tests undertaken at specified intervals during the storage life of the mine, to illustrate that the efficiency and effectiveness of the mine remain unimpaired. It will be apparent that considerable time and effort, and hence expense, are invested in providing a high level of safety in mines. Without question they must be safe to store, transport, lay and arm. It is desirable, if not always essential, that they are safe to disarm for re-use or clearance. Expenditure on achieving safety objectives will enhance the utility of mines by generating confidence in the minds of their potential users. Soldiers will readily be prepared to employ such devices, if they are assured that there is negligible risk to themselves. It is important, and in their own interest, that designers and manufacturers continue to sustain this belief as an unquestionable fact.

Reliability

During the period that vast quantities of cheap and simple mines were relied upon to provide a barrier, the individual reliability of each mine was not vital, provided that collectively the mines achieved their purpose. In fact, the simplicity of purely mechanical, pressure operated devices normally allowed a very high level of mine reliability to be assured. As second generation mines became more complex, their reliability was not so easily guaranteed, in view of the sophistication of their warheads and the intricacy of their fuzes and sensors. And this tendency will continue into third generation devices. But the advent of computer aided design and manufacturing, coupled to the rigorous testing and trialling mentioned above, can assist in ensuring that the mine remains a reliable device. This will become more and more essential as the cost and importance of the individual mine rises. For example, we have seen that fewer influence fuzed, FWA devices are needed than contact mines to achieve the same stopping power. Thus each of these FWA mines has a larger area of responsibility, or footprint, than its pressure sensitive predecessor and its failure to operate will leave a correspondingly larger gap in the minefield to be exploited by an enemy. This far, we have been considering reliability in terms of functioning and operability, however, there are two additional components of reliability that need to be examined further.

The first is selectivity. A mine's sensor system must not allow the warhead to be wasted, either through false initiation or as a result of complete passivity. The fuze window must be optimized for attack of the primary, high value target. In other words, AP mines should not be so sensitive that a rabbit will detonate them, or AT mines so crude that they cannot identify between lorries and AFVs. In addition, the sensors should not be vulnerable to deception by counter-measures. If the fuzing system can accomplish the necessary target sensitivity through the application of thresholds or logic gates, then the second factor comes into play. This is lethality. The succesful engagement arises from accuracy and terminal effect, the former allowing the warhead to reach a vulnerable point on the target and the latter permitting an overmatch of the target's protection at that point. In the case of an AP mine of the bounding type, reliable accuracy would be achieved by detonation of the mine once targets are within range and at a height that maximizes the possibility of a hit, whilst the reliability of the warhead depends upon the effect of the fragments on the enemy soldiers. For an AT mine, the warhead should attack the mid-third of the vehicle and overcome the armour with

PLATE 5.1. *An anti-personnel jumping mine with pressure sensitive prongs and a trip-wire sensor.*

PLATE 5.2. *A command detonated, area fragmentation mine made by FFV of Sweden.*

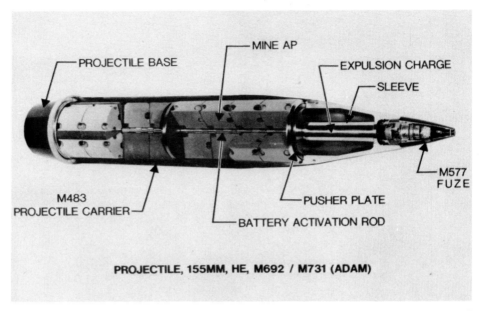

PLATE 5.3. *One configuration for the remote delivery of AP mines from within a 155-millimetre artillery cargo shell.*

PLATE 5.4. *The Ranger anti-personnel scatterable mine system, which can be fitted to a wide variety of vehicles and boats.*

PLATE 5.5. *A shallow-water mine to protect coasts and river banks.*

PLATE 5.6. *The HB 876 area denial mine with a combined plate charge and fragmentation warhead. Note the steel spring, orientation arms.*

PLATE 5.7. *Tornado, providing fast and accurate delivery of JP 233 airfield denial munitions.*

PLATE 5.8. *Smoke or puff mines are a valuable aid to mine warfare training.*

PLATE 5.9. *Inert replicas of mines serve as the basis of recognition training and ensure safety in arming and disarming drills.*

PLATE 5.10. *Coloured smoke and flashing lights show that this AFV has been caught in a minefield simulated with lasers.*

PLATE 5.11. *A laser anti-tank weapon simulator, capable of being adapted to form the basis of a minefield simulation system.*

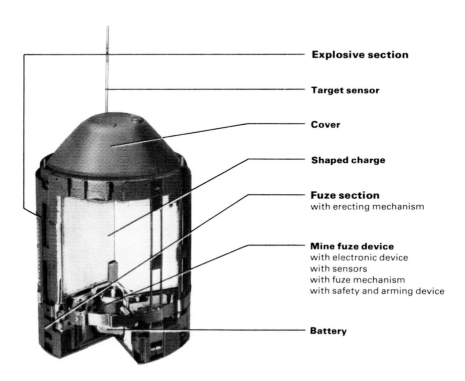

Explosive section

Target sensor

Cover

Shaped charge

Fuze section
with erecting mechanism

Mine fuze device
with electronic device
with sensors
with fuze mechanism
with safety and arming device

Battery

PLATE 6.1. *The AT2 scatterable mine can be delivered by MLRS, multi-barrel rocket launcher or vehicle dispenser.*

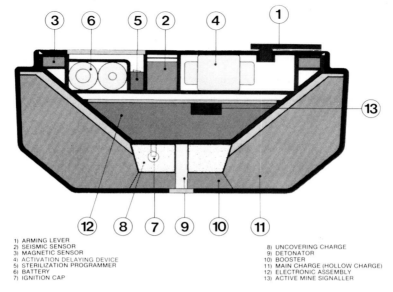

1) ARMING LEVER
2) SEISMIC SENSOR
3) MAGNETIC SENSOR
4) ACTIVATION DELAYING DEVICE
5) STERILIZATION PROGRAMMER
6) BATTERY
7) IGNITION CAP

8) UNCOVERING CHARGE
9) DETONATOR
10) BOOSTER
11) MAIN CHARGE (HOLLOW CHARGE)
12) ELECTRONIC ASSEMBLY
13) ACTIVE MINE SIGNALLER

PLATE 6.2. *A modern, hollow charge mine with a magnetic influence fuze.*

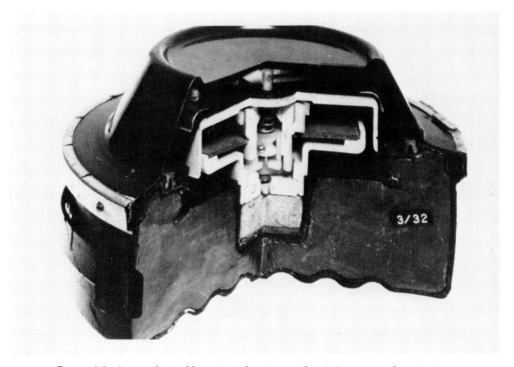

PLATE 6.3. *A non-detectable anti-tank mine, with minimum metal content.*

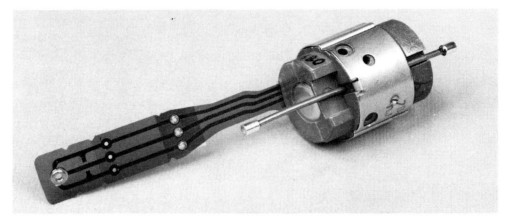

PLATE 6.4. *A safety and arming device for a scatterable AP mine.*

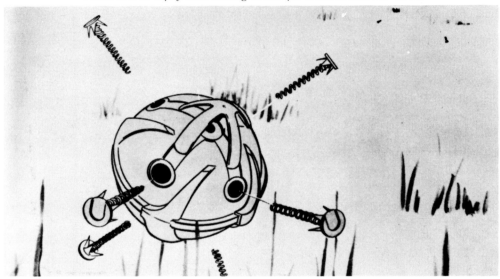

PLATE 6.5. *An anti-personnel mine concept, showing trip lines being deployed from a scatterable mine.*

PLATE 6.6. *Mechanical handling equipment is essential to the re-supply of mines on the battlefield.*

sufficient power remaining to damage the interior of the MBT. Even though a mine may function as a system, it could not be considered reliable if, taking an AT mine as an example, it had a propensity to attack the rear of an AFV with insufficient power to penetrate the armour, or a tendency to detonate when the minefield is under artillery fire. In the view of the soldier behind the minefield, lethality and target selectivity are just as much aspects of reliability as the ability of the device to function properly as a mechanism.

Economy

Mines are traditionally inexpensive and have been referred to as "the poor man's weapon". This is an unfortunate description as, although cheap individually, the numbers of mines that have been purchased have required considerable investment from the purchasing nation. As the price of mines increases, the percentage of military budgets allocated to mine warfare is unlikely to rise in the same proportion. Consequently, fewer mines will be purchased and the danger is that, despite the increased effectiveness of new mines, the mine warfare capability of the force could decrease overall. To prevent this, a designer must be conscious of the need for economy. Sensors, fuzes and warheads need to be designed to achieve their purpose without recourse to the most expensive devices, or the use of the most advanced technology. Adequacy and sufficiency should be the guide-lines. On the warhead side, these parameters should prevent over-powerful devices from being produced. The mine only needs to be capable of defeating its primary target, and whilst a small measure of over-match is desirable to meet possible target enhancements, this precaution should not be pursued to the detriment of an economical design.

Simplicity

The technology of second and third generation mines is likely to be based on sensitive sensors, intelligent fuzes and rapid signal processing. Internally, these devices will be technically advanced, externally, however, the mines must appear as uncomplicated as ever. The minimum manual interface is required to reduce training time, to improve laying rates and to facilitate mechanical or remote delivery. In addition to being simple to operate, the mines must be so designed as to be capable of mass production. To an extent this consideration also encompasses the principles of economy and reliability, because the manufacture of reliable mines, affording economy through large production runs, is dependent upon an elegant and reproducible engineering design.

Counter-measures

The mine and potential counter-measures to it are indivisible parts of a whole. Once a designer has a concept for his mine, he must immediately consider how to include protection against general counter-measures likely to be used against it. The first thought might be how to simplify its concealment, and this will lead to a desire to minimize size, especially height, and specify an appropriate matt colour finish. Some mines can be bought in sandy yellow casings for desert use, for example, and the UK Dingbat AP mine was issued in a camouflaged hessian purse that blended into almost any vegetation background. Determined clearance or breaching parties will use prodders and detectors to locate mines. One or two mines have been produced that detonate when impacted by a mine prodder, although these are rare, as their extreme sensitivity is generally considered a dangerous disadvantage. Much more common is the non-detectable design, based upon a plastic construction, with the absolute minimum of metal content — normally a tiny spring or detonator capsule. Beyond these fundamental qualities of size, shape, colour and material, other counter-measure resistant properties can be built in. These may be anti-handling, anti-disturbance, or explosive shock resistance, but are not so much design principles as requirements specified by the purchaser. Nevertheless, the need to make a mine difficult to see, detect and counter is a vital element in the design process, having a significant effect on the eventual form which the mine takes.

Durability

Unlike other munitions, there is no way of turning-over the extensive stocks of mines that are held. They are expected to lie dormant in ammunition depots for many years and then operate first time when required to do so. This shelf-life is often stated as a minimum of 10 years and can be as much as 20 years. Indeed, the UK Mk VII mine is well over that limit and the US M1 mines used by the Argentinians on the Falklands were manufactured in the closing stages of World War II. The longevity seen as an essential element of the mine is matched by the emphasis placed on mine toughness. Stored and transported in large numbers, often in a time of emergency, there is little opportunity for consideration to be given to their careful handling. Once their rough journey is over, the worst conditions have yet to be faced. Mechanical, scatterable or remote delivery will test the strength of the case and components and then the environment will challenge those that have withstood the experiences up to that point. The mine must, above all, be waterproof to repel ground moisture, rain, dew and snow. In alternative, extreme climes it may have to withstand great heat, or icy cold too. However, the final trial for the AT mine is probably the greatest. It is difficult to imagine the effect of a tank track on a mine; whatever may be envisaged the mine must not disintegrate or collapse and has to remain intact to function at the right moment. Durability in a mine, comprising longevity and toughness, is thus a vital design objective.

Packaging

Driven by the demand to reduce the logistic burden and to improve delivery and laying rates, the total packaging concept for the mine has to be considered from early in the design stage. The result of this type of forethought can be seen in the MISAR SB 33 and SB 81 mines, which are purchased in special magazines. These are suitable for storing and transport, simplify hand laying and are compatible with vehicle and helicopter mounted dispensers. This sort of lead needs to be followed for all future systems, to reduce the problems of handling and disposing of excess packaging, packing pieces and containers. These items consume space in storage and during transport, require time and manpower to deal with them, and are difficult to conceal on the battlefield, providing an obvious indication that mining operations are, or were, under way in the vicinity. Efforts to eliminate these problems through careful design will be worthwhile and make a positive contribution to the ultimate effectiveness of the whole mine system.

Possible Enhancements

Remote Control

One of the most attractive options for the operational commander that modern mine technology can offer is that of remote control, in the sense that he can order mined areas to be switched on when danger threatens, or off when he wishes to pass his forces through them. The Soviet, remotely-armed mines of World War II have been mentioned previously and terrorist road mines in Ulster are usually fired from a remoted position, either by cable or radio signal. Thus the practicality of such devices has been amply demonstrated. There are varying degrees of remote control, the simplest and probably most feasible one in the near future is the ability to switch a mine on, into the armed state. To switch repeatedly on and off, with the degree of confidence required that the mine is indeed disarmed, is a much more demanding and expensive requirement. One proposal to strengthen the confidence that the mine is not in a live state, is that the mine should be able to respond to instructions or interrogation through its own transmitter and advise the controller of its armed or disarmed condition. To reach this stage of refinement will be costly and may be unnecessary. Indeed, to field mines with the simplest variety of remote control will be quite an achievement. The first hurdle will be to bring into service an electronic safety and arming unit (SAU) that is acceptable to safety boards for use in land mines. Whilst electronic SAUs are commonplace in guided weapons, none have been devised to meet the ruggedness and cheapness expected of mine components. Once such an SAU exists the problem of controlling its function remotely, for example by radio, is simplified. However, this radio link in itself introduces new dilemmas, for the mine must be capable of discriminating its particular and specific instruction to arm from amongst the many other radiations on the battlefield. This must be achieved in such a way as to ensure that the mines are never armed by a random signal. In the same fashion, the mines must be resistant to deliberate measures by an enemy to arm them unbeknown to the defenders or to render them inoperative by jamming or overloading the receivers. The likely cost of fuzes responsive to remote instructions will almost certainly limit the numbers purchased and this may be viewed as a sensible limitation, for it would be unwise to invest heavily in a type of mine which could fall prey to an enemy's electronic warfare attack. If numbers of remotely controlled mines were limited, this would also overcome the problem of ensuring that all mines in large fields had actually received the instructions meant for them. Those few mines with a remote, switch-on facility would be reserved for use in closing gaps or lanes in minefields, or in selective ambushes, where it could be guaranteed that the control signals can be received at the mine. Such mines would provide a rapid and effective solution to the major problem at present of how to close minefields in the face of the enemy, possibly after friendly forces had just withdrawn through them.

Programmable Arming

FWA influence fuzes and anti-disturbance mines present a hazard to the laying team when delivered mechanically, since laying the next row may activate the influence fuze, or a breakdown in the layer or towing vehicle could cause armed mines to remain in the layer. To avert the possibility of such incidents arising, second generation mines are often provided with a delayed arming sequence. The time that the mines remain unarmed can vary from several minutes to a few hours. The timing devices presently employed are either mechanical or electronic, being pre-set during manufacture. This allows no flexibility in the operational area, where a shorter or longer arming delay could be desirable in a specific situation. Consequently, a programmable delay is seen to have operational advantages. However this was configured would have to be compatible with mechanical or remote laying, whereby the desired time would be set into the layer or dispenser by the operator, and the mine fuzes would then be programmed through the dispenser. Infinitely variable programming is unlikely to be affordable, whilst the option of several pre-set timings is likely to meet the operational demand and be technically achievable at an acceptable cost. An extension of programmable arming is the automatic switching on and off of mines according to a selected sequence. Such a characteristic could have applications, say, on an airfield where protecting AP minefields may only be required to come into play during the hours of darkness. This capability is unlikely to be available until variable arming delay has been fully accepted and proven.

Self Neutralization

The introduction of electronics into mine fuzes permitted a requirement to be met that had long been considered desirable, particularly in the context of SM and RDM. This was the ability of the mine to neutralize itself, either through sterilization or destruction. The removal of any danger from the mine to friendly forces is considered useful, especially in mobile warfare where the defending troops may wish to move through a previously mined area. As we shall see, one of the great difficulties introduced by rapid mine laying and SM or RDM is that of minefield reporting. It is almost impossible to ensure that every unit, squad or vehicle is up-dated on mines laid in their vicinity or where they may be moving to. The uncertainty over the exact location of RDM is even greater. Thus to prevent casualties from their own mines, it is thought desirable by some forces to build-in a time, after which the device renders itself useless. Other armies may prefer to have mines that self-destruct. Although it is obvious to the observer that a self-destruct mine has exploded, offering a high degree of confidence that the area can be crossed safely, it does allow an enemy exactly the same opportunity. Consequently, self-sterilization is preferred when the enemy has to be kept guessing as to the armed state of the minefields. However, a consideration in favour of self-destruct mines is that a destroyed mine can not be re-used against the original owner. In anti-guerrilla warfare this is an important factor and could prevent self-sterilization fuzes being adopted. Another benefit of mines that can detonate themselves is the danger that such destruction poses to anybody near the mine. Variable self-destruct times amongst each batch of mines will cause individual devices to explode at irregular intervals, providing a considerable deterrent to breaching parties.

Cheap, but reliable, digital clocks have made self-neutralization entirely feasible. Many current mines do, and most future ones will, have this capability, although it could be limited to fixed and pre-set live periods. This will certainly be the case if the point of neutralization is determined by mechanical means or is dependent upon the discharge of the power supply battery. Using an entirely electronic timer will allow variable neutralization, that can be programmed prior to laying, to meet the prevailing operational requirement.

Scatterability

Perhaps the most important innovation in mine warfare recently has been the move away from traditional minelaying techniques to scattering and remote delivery. Normally, SM have less of a rugged launch environment than RDM, and a lower, likely impact force. Nevertheless, they might be hurled 50 metres from a cartridge tube or dropped 200 metres from a helicopter, so they do have to be tough. At present most SM are pressure fuzed and the components are easily ruggedized from durable plastic. The mines tend to be shallow and disc shaped, with sloping sides ensuring that the mine lies on its top or bottom face. Delayed arming will ensure that the fuze does not register the force of the landing and detonate. Once armed, it is irrelevant to the fuze which way the mine is orientated since the sensor will activate, whether the pressure plate is depressed into the mine or the mine is pressed down on to the plate.

It is remote delivery, which provides the greatest challenges to mine technology. To begin with, the severity of the launch is considerable. Probably the worst case is for gun delivered munitions, which experience extremely high acceleration and spin rates. As RDM tend to be influence fuzed devices, their electronic components and sensors have to be firmly mounted and protected against the set-back forces of the gun. This is normally achieved by encasing sensitive components in a rigid plastic cake — a process known as potting. Air and rocket delivered mines would be provided with similar protection for their electronic assemblies. After release from the delivery vessel, be it shell, container rocket or free-fall container, the individual mines have to be stabilized in flight to provide a distribution on the ground which offers the required density. Equally, the mine velocity has to be retarded to a level that will prevent the mine shattering or malfunctioning. These two requirements could be met by providing the mine with fins, a small inflatable bag, a parachute or drogue. This retardation device can also be used to orientate the mine on landing, but most designs incorporate a separate self-righting mechanism. Such an aid will allow the retardation device to be ejected away from the RDM, since it might otherwise compromise the location of the mine.

The need for an orientation device is dictated by the form of the warhead. RDM are presently belly attack weapons with either shaped or plate charge warheads. The hot jet or kinetic projectile from these mines is most effective when fired perpendicular to the target, so the self-righting device should perch the mine in an upright position, whatever the type of terrain. This is especially important for a single-ended warhead, that is, a mine that can only fire from one of its faces. Double-ended devices can fire from either face and would, on first sight, appear to be a preferable solution. However, within the same volume more explosive energy can be channelled behind a uni-directional weapon than to either warhead of a similarly sized, double-ended mine. As RDM are restricted in size by the dimensions of their dispensers and the desire to deliver the maximum number of them in any given carrier, the very best effect should be sought from each mine. This is offered by the single-ended mine with an orientation device fitted. These self-righting mechanisms have to occupy minimum space and weight, and the most common solution has been to utilize slim, spring steel arms or coronets to flick the mine into an effective firing position.

Mention has been made of other desirable characteristics of mines, particularly variable arming and self-neutralization, which have special relevance to SM and RDM. Such mines are contained in sealed carriers, like shells, and a data interface is necessary to program the mine fuzes. This can be achieved through instruments known as presetters. These are electronic devices that can be fed the required fuze information once, to be held in the instrument's memory, and then released repeatedly to the mines via a data link through the container. A feature that could be especially useful to SM and RDM is an anti-handling or anti-disturbance mode to prevent breaching and clearance when the mines are laid beyond observation of defending forces. This may not always be desirable and a fuze that permitted the selection of whether or not the anti-lift option was in effect could be valuable. The instruction specifying the chosen option could be transmitted through the presetter too.

Mine Components

Essential Sub-assemblies

The body or case of a mine usually contains the whole device, although some sensors may be outside the main casing, and off-route or area mines with their trip-wires, stands and remote control cables do not fit easily into this generalization. However, all mines have sensors. These vary from simple pressure pads through fibre optic loops to microprocessor controlled magnetometers. The information from the sensors is transmitted to the fuze, which contains the safety and arming unit (SAU), the power supply, the firing actuator and an explosive, or detonation, train. The SAU is the control centre of the mine. It is here that all the safety interlocks are found, which come into play when the safety pins or tabs are removed and the arming sequence commences. The power for the mine in its passive, waiting state is normally very small, just enough to keep an alerter sensor operational. When the alerter considers a target is approaching, more energy is required to activate the main sensor or fire control system. And at the moment of attack, a great boost of electrical power is needed to fire the warhead. This process could take place several days after laying and perhaps many years after the mine was originally made. Thus the provision of a sealed power supply for mines, with a considerable shelf-life and the ability to function in a temperature range from as low as −30°C up to +40°C, is by no means a simple technical achievement. The answer over recent years has been to use reserve cell batteries based on lithium compounds, an area of technology which is constantly advancing. The firing actuator is the assembly causing the detonator to explode, and can vary from a striker mechanism for percussion caps to an electronic amplifier circuit for electrical detonators. Detonators in mines tend to be very small and their initiation is only the first step in the explosive train, for there is normally a booster charge between them and the main explosive content. It is also common for modern mines to have what is known as a clearance charge. To reduce the total size of the mine, sensors and parts of the fuze are often placed into the hollow space in a shaped or plate charge warhead. However, the efficiency of such attack mechanisms is entirely dependent upon there being an empty volume ahead of the main charge. Thus the components sitting in there have to be cleared away. Equally, if the mine has been laid beneath the surface, any cover or earth must be removed from the path of the attack, otherwise the formation of the hot gases or fragment could be inhibited or their energy dissipated. In mines with clearance charges, the sequence of operation of the explosive train would be for the first detonator to fire a clearance charge that removed the contents of the hollow part of the warhead plus any earth covering, followed within a fraction of a microsecond by a second detonator initiating a booster charge to explode the warhead itself. Warhead technology is an entire subject in itself and an outline of the types of warhead in use will be presented later in this chapter. Although sensors, casing, fuze and warhead are the major components of a mine, one final area of applicable technology must be mentioned and this is the packaging concept. Referred to previously under design principles, the importance of a whole-life, packaging policy for mines cannot be over-emphasized. If ignored, the advantages of improved mine effectiveness and more rapid means of delivery or laying will be negated by cumbersome, unimaginative and wasteful handling and unpacking procedures.

Sensors

There is a very wide range of sensors available for use with mines, and more are on the technical horizon. The choice of which type will be used is dependent upon a variety of factors: the target, the type of warhead, the cost, the means of delivery, enemy counter-measures and the tactical use envisaged for the mine. Some nations have a preference for many simple mines, others consider that fewer more complex devices offer better value for money. Undoubtedly, the greatest variety and most advanced of sensors are found in the US inventory. The following review, however, covers sensors that can be found world-wide, but it is unlikely that any one nation has examples of all in service.

Whilst remote control is not exactly a sensor, it needs to be included for completeness. It can be as simple as lashing a shoulder fired LAW to a tree and pulling the trigger with a length of cord, when a tank passes by. Slightly more complex is firing a land mine through an electrical detonator, connected by insulated cable to a battery or dynamo. This sort of arrangement is also used to detonate AP area mines, such as the FFV 013 fragmentation mine. The use of radio signals to command detonate mines has been demonstrated in terrorist situations, and military forces are purchasing remote firing devices to initiate demolitions. These are transmitters/receivers operating over several hundred metres on coded frequencies, having obvious applications in the remote control of electrically detonated mines.

Over shorter distances, the "trip-wire" range of sensors have been frequently employed. Initially, an extremely thin, tough wire would have been used to snag a foot or catch a wheel, and detonate the mine it was connected to. Traditionally, the narrow steel or nylon strand has been used to fire AP mines. To attack vehicles, the trip-wire concept was developed for use with ORMs in particular, however, the US M612 pneumatic pressure fuze with a 3-metre hose was used with buried mines. Many variations on the theme have been displayed, an early type being the pressure responsive, electrical discriminator deployed with the US M24 rocket based ORM. A vehicle crossing the pressure switch cable completes the electrical circuit and fires the rocket motor igniter. The more advanced M66 mine, using the same anti-tank rocket, employs an IR beam across the likely path of the target. The beam is formed between a transmitter and receiver, both mounted on tripods, and carefully aligned to ensure a constant signal. When the beam is broken by a target, the circuit collapses, firing the missile into the side of the vehicle. Disruption of an electrical circuit is also the basis of frangible wire sensors. These are extremely thin, conductive break wires, as used with the French MIACAH ORM or MIAPED fragmentation mine, which are easily ruptured when traversed by a heavy vehicle or dragged by a careless shin. The most advanced sensor in this series is probably that issued with the Bundeswehr's Remote Action Mine. Commonly called the PARM 1 it is an ORM with a unique, optical fibre, sensor cable. Vehicle pressure on the optical fibre distorts the light signal, activating the shaped charge warhead. Whilst all of these trip-wire type sensors can be effectively camouflaged, and prove difficult to see either on foot or from a vehicle, they suffer from several disadvantages. They do, for example, require to be set out carefully by fully trained personnel. This is inevitably time-consuming, and once laid the sensors are vulnerable to simple counter-measures. However, the most limiting factor can be considered to be the range of the sensor. The range is restricted to the maximum length of cable that the sensor system can operate over, being typically less than 60 metres. Compared to the potential range of the ORM kill mechanisms, this is very restrictive, leading to the requirement for a new type of sensor.

The solution to extended range for enhanced ORM has come in two principal forms. One depends on IR, the other on radar. Within the IR possibilities, active IR has proven unpopular of late as it has become so easy to detect and, therefore, simple to locate the source of the radiation. Passive IR, on the other hand, is undetectable and virtually invulnerable to realistic counter-measures. The recent emphasis on Thermal Imaging technology in military research and development has allowed valuable technical spin-off to be utilized in less complex passive IR sensors. The effectiveness of such sensors in measuring the thermal differential induced by a tank has been successfully demonstrated in the United Kingdom, with targets engaged at various crossing speeds and different ranges. The same technology has been considered as the basis for sensing devices on future ORM in France and Germany, and indeed GIAT of France have offered the IRMAH passive IR sensor to be used with the MIACAH ORM for several years now. Whilst European developers appear to favour the less expensive and passive IR systems, the concepts appearing in the United States show a preference for the more costly and active radar sensors based upon microwave or millimetric wave technology. Perhaps this is as a result of the considerable investment there into the areas of top attack weapons and target seeking sub-munitions, many of which would utilize millimetre wave (MMW) sensors. Thus, expertise in this technology is probably more advanced in the United States than elsewhere and new outlets, such as mine sensors, are sought in an attempt to recover the costs of the initial research effort. The new Motorola WASPM, side-attack ORM utilizes an MMW sensor to guide its warhead on to crossing targets at ranges in excess of 60 metres. Very high hit probability can be expected from these sensing devices as they are able to track the target through its radar echo and predict its position accurately at the moment of attack by the mine. Their other great advantage is that they are virtually weather independent, able to sense and track targets through rain, fog, snow and the dust or smoke of battle. However, they are active devices and this does leave them open to detection. Just as MBT once carried IR detectors to warn them of active IR surveillance, and military aircraft now carry electronic warfare pods to alert them to radar trackers, then future AFVs could carry MMW detectors to signal the presence of short wave radar transmissions. The opportunity for counter-measures to be applied would be a similar disadvantage for two further, as yet unfielded types of mine sensors: laser and active ultrasonic devices. Lasers are presently employed in a variety of weapon systems, the most relevant being the laser transceiver used for range finding in many MBT fire control systems. It is not outside the bounds of possibility that lasers could provide a third option as an ORM sensor in competition with MMW and passive IR. The ultrasonic device, a land based sonar, would add further choice to the possibilities. Yet all of these types of sensor have one factor in common, they consume relatively high levels of electrical energy during operation. This rate of power consumption could not be sustained throughout the required operational life of the mine by current, reserve cell batteries, and a switch-on/switch-off policy is consequently employed.

Power management is achieved by linking alerter sensors to the mine's data processor. Such processors are an essential component of second generation mines, needed to control the essential safety and arming functions plus the fire control computations for the main sensors. The alerters are very similar to the remote battlefield sensor systems deployed ahead of, or in gaps between, defensive posts to warn the defenders of enemy approach. The alert sensors are usually microphones or geophones, utilizing acoustic or seismic signatures to discriminate between people, animals and vehicles and, if possible, to identify the various types of vehicle. Thus, the main sensor would lie dormant, utilizing no power, whilst the alerter sensor remains awake, but operating on minimal power. Once the alerter feeds signals to the processor, which indicate that a suitable target for the mine is approaching and within range, the main sensor is activated and an engagement can take place. If the mine does not attack, perhaps because the target is seen to be out of range of the kill mechanism or it changes direction away from the mine's area of influence, then the main sensor will be switched off until the next target appears. Alerters are also required for the majority of the final group of sensors, those utilized in influence fuzes.

The term influence sensor rightly suggests that the target is in close proximity to the mine and its sensor. All existing influence fuzes have limited range and usually rely upon the shadow of the target falling over the mine to induce an attack. The exception to this rule is the tentacle type of sensor dispensed from the AP mines in the US FASCAM programme. These trip-line tentacles are deployed by spring action after the mine has settled on the ground and are sensitive to the slightest disturbance being transmitted to the trembler switch. Another sensor depending upon contact as its influence is the tilt fuze, as used on the powerful US M21 "Killer" AT mine, the Czech plate charge mine or the UK Mk 7 AT mine. The length of the vertical mast is usually 60 to 90 centimetres, allowing it to be deflected by the edge of an MBT glacis plate. This movement could either cause a rod to fracture within the mast, releasing a detonator striker, or the rigid mast might tilt a pressure plate at its base, causing the mine to initiate. Since tilt fuzes tend to be used in the belly attack role, a brief time delay is often built in to the detonation chain, allowing the mine to explode farther under the hull of the moving target. The tilt rod concept can also be applied to AP mines, as in the Dutch No. 23 bounding mine, which responds to a push or pull on its short, stub mast.

More modern influence fuzes, to be found in second generation FWA mines, are dependent upon advanced electronics to analyse acoustic, seismic, magnetic or thermal signals generated by potential targets. The alerter sensors would provide broad target recognition and cause the main sensor to switch-on. This takes over from the alerter, measuring the strength or frequency of target signals, thereby allowing the microprocessor to determine the most opportune moment for the kill mechanism to strike at the mid-third of the AFV's belly. The preferred type of sensor at present is that based on magnetic effects. Every vehicle has a magnetic signature arising from its metal mass, power pack and electrical system. Whilst there is a unique signal for a particular vehicle, similar types of vehicle will have a broadly common signature pattern. Consequently, the mine can be programmed to recognize and react to the particular type of pattern generated by the principal target for the mine. The same is true of the acoustic signals from a vehicle's engine, exhaust and tracks. However, the potential for interference from background combat noise has led to a questioning of the reliability of acoustic sensors for precision instrumentation. Similarly, the difficulties of analysing the confusing seismic signals from a tracked vehicle, signals which travel both over the surface and through the ground, have prevented the successful introduction of a seismic sensor. Nevertheless, the availability of new and powerful micro-processors and processing techniques will enable the problems of analysis to be overcome and permit seismic devices to be introduced as principal mine sensors. Nor have thermal detectors yet been accepted as the sensor for a surface or buried mine. This is surprising in view of the knowledge and expertise now available in electro-optic and heat seeking technologies. But perhaps manufacturers are satisfied with the current range of magnetic influence fuzes and see no improvement in performance being achieved by the introduction of new sensors. There are, however, good military reasons to introduce different or extra sensing devices and these will be proposed in a later chapter. For the present, it is time to consider the other major component of a mine which can take a great variety of forms — the warhead.

Warhead Options

The lethal, kill or attack mechanism may be a better description of that part of the mine, which actually attacks the target, than warhead, since many of the attack mechanisms can not be easily visualized as warheads. For example, the long slab of explosive known as the Barmine can hardly be described in a similar vein to the sleek-nosed warhead of a tactical nuclear missile. However, common usage has allowed the term to be adopted in mine warfare and the practice will be perpetuated here.

Originally, the mine depended upon the blast of a high explosive (HE) charge for its effect. This was, and remains, true for both AT and AP mines. The majority of mines in service probably continue to rely upon blast to attack their targets, just as they depend upon pressure as their means of actuation. HE is very effective in the mine role, possessing the power in acceptable quantities to slice through a heavy tank track and to severely injure the feet or legs of soldiers, even when present in only small amounts. This effectiveness has much to do with three parallel developments. The first area of improvement has been in the explosives themselves. TNT was first prepared in the middle of the nineteenth century, yet continued to be used as a filling for mines during World War II along with Amatol or Picric acid. It is now unusual to find these as the main charges in mines, having been replaced in many countries by an improved explosive — RDX. This is a more powerful composition, developed during World War II, and adopted widely as an excellent explosive compound. The Warsaw Pact states probably do not have access to RDX, but must have introduced their own replacement for earlier explosives, just as the United States may prefer to use their development, Composition B, in US mines. All of these main charges consist of secondary explosives, which are stable, heat resistant and generally insensitive to impact and shock, whilst having a latent, high energy output.

To release this HE energy, initiatory or primary explosives are used to boost the power released by the detonator to a level sufficient to initiate the main charge. Correct detonation is the second improvement to have taken place. As a general rule detonation and initiation should occur in the direction in which the main blast is required. The detonation wave moves like a weather front through the secondary explosive, forcing the explosion before it, and hopefully reinforcing the blast effect towards the target. Wave shaping, detonation management, placing the detonator, booster and main charge in the optimum position with respect to

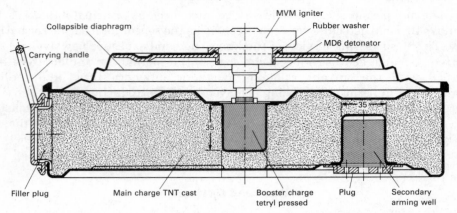

FIG. 6.1. *This basic construction of the Soviet TMN 46 anti-vehicle mine has formed the basis of many derivatives throughout the world.*

one another and the target, have allowed designers to obtain the maximum effect from the contained explosive. The final area of parallel development has been in the production area. Improved manufacturing techniques have ensured higher quality explosives and more reliable, predictable detonators, whilst closer attention to filling mines with main charges has virtually eliminated the problems of shrinkage, cracking and density gradients — all of which would degrade the design performance of the mine.

Fragmentation warheads, of course, depend for their correct actuation on similar considerations to those above. In some respects even more so, for the explosive energy has to be directed and controlled to force the fragments out into their required trajectory. And a specific trajectory is certainly expected, as little is

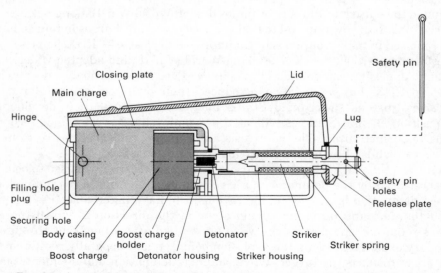

FIG. 6.2. *A typical box mine, simple and easy to manufacture but still effective.*

left to chance in the fine calculations undertaken during the design process. At the initial design stage a choice has to be made on the size and shape of the fragments. They have to be a certain minimum weight, firstly to overcome the air resistance, and then to provide an appreciable wound. Three hundred milligrams is probably as small as is acceptable for a short range, bounding mine, whilst fragments of five hundred milligrams are needed for area defence mines. The shape has an effect on both range and lethality. Area mines, such as the FFV 013 and US M18 are expected to have a fairly good range, say out to 100 metres. To achieve this the fragments need a good ballistic shape, which is why these mines utilize steel balls embedded in a plastic honeycomb. For the very reason that this is a good shape for range, it is a poor shape for wounding, because the worst wounds are caused by an unstable fragment tumbling inside the body. Such a shape is provided by the fragmentation of a prenotched case, chopped bar or scored wire body. Thus, in general, the shorter range, jumping mines would employ fragments produced by this latter range of casings, with a high wounding capability. Of course, the effectiveness of shrapnel type mines depends not simply on the individual particles expelled, but the collective damage induced by a large number of such fragments attacking the target simultaneously. The area AP mines referred to earlier could contain a thousand steel balls, fired into an arc no greater than 1000 mils. Despite the relative inefficiency of each pellet, the total number of strikes on a man-size target is sufficient to inflict mortal wounds at less than 50 metres and incapacitating injury at greater ranges. To achieve the correct distribution of fragments is, therefore, fundamental to the design of the mine and this depends upon correct directional initiation of the right amount and shape of explosive. Whilst a terrorist can fabricate some sort of fragmentation mine from nails embedded in plastic explosive, the munition manufacturer has to show consistency, accuracy and reliability in repeated firing trials of his mine.

High proficiency in explosives technology is also at the heart of the three remaining types of warhead to be discussed. All are AT devices and are sometimes linked together under the term Chemical Energy Attack. There is certainly a common thread running through them, although the resultant defeat of armour arises from a different effect for each of them. The reader can judge for himself how they should be categorized after this brief review.

Terminology is the first stumbling block to be overcome in describing the most frequently encountered AT warhead, that dependent upon the shaped charge effect. Also called a hollow, Monroe or Neumann charge, it forms the basis of HEAT (high explosive, anti-tank) munitions. It has long been used in LAW or ATGW warheads and MBT main armament rounds, but is only just coming into extensive use in surface or buried mines as a result of the demand for belly attack devices. It is also employed as the attack mechanism in ORM such as the M66, PARM1, and Lawmine. As the name suggests, the explosive charge is shaped into a hollow cone. A liner is provided to this cone, possibly of copper or aluminium. The charge is initiated from the base and, with the aid of a detonation wave shaper, the explosive energy is focused along the axis of the cone. The liner collapses into this axis too, enhancing the powerful, penetrative jet, which slices through armour as a narrow beam of hot gas and molten metal. Stand-off is important to this type of attack as the jet needs time and space to form, but this is of no disadvantage to a mine charge that lies on or just below ground and has the tank hull clearance distance to traverse before meeting the belly armour. An interesting appreciation of the need for stand-off between the shaped charge and its target was displayed in a very crude device used by the Japanese in World War II. Called a suicide lunge mine by the Allies, it consisted of a short stick, at one end of which was a simple hollow charge — the whole resembling a drain plunger or oil funnel. However, from the flat face of the charge protruded three sharp prongs. The Japanese soldier would attack an Allied tank with this affair, the prongs providing both purchase on the armour and stand-off for the charge, the latter being detonated by a striker forced home as the soldier lunged with the stick handle. As crude and suicidal as the mine might have been, it proved quite capable of boring through 100 millimetres of tank armour. And this penetrative capability of relatively small amounts of shaped explosive, is the reason why hollow charge munitions remain in worldwide service to this day.

A similarly universal type of warhead is that employing the plate charge effect. This too has several names including Miznay-Schardin and P Charge. The effect is based upon explosively propelling a metal plate with sufficient energy to punch a hole through protective armour. Normally, the plate is slightly dished and presses into the propellant explosive, away from the target. After the charge has detonated, the dishing on the plate is inevitably reversed and often exaggerated, as if the plate had been reformed by giant hands into a rough metal slug. At short ranges this slug can penetrate the side armour of MBT when fired from ORMs of the French MIACAH type. Interestingly, the Czech plate charge mine can be rotated in its frame to be either a belly attack or horizontal effect mine. When aimed at the belly of an AFV from devices such as the Czech or the US M21 "Killer" mine it has catastrophic effects on the vehicle interior. Not only does the deformed plate crash about inside the target, but all the displaced armour fragments act as destructive missiles within the confines of the armoured compartment too. These behind-armour effects are usually greater for plate charges than shaped charges, since the latter produce purely linear consequences that may or may not strike a vulnerable or volatile point within the target. However, for a given diameter the plate charge would only penetrate half the armour that a similarly dimensioned shaped charge could defeat.

The third type of warhead in this series is an obvious derivative of the second. It can possibly be viewed as the modern or ultimate development of a Miznay-Schardin device; it is the self forging fragment (SFF) warhead, sometimes called the Explosion Forged Projectile (EFP). SFF technology has improved as a consequence of the research impetus into top attack weapons, but has an obvious application in FWA mines and ORM, probably being the preferred kill mechanism for the new US WASPM. The principle behind SFF is the same as that for plate charge attack, with a shaped metal plate or liner being propelled and deformed by an explosive charge. In this case, the components are configured to produce a much more streamlined projectile, reminiscent of a spearhead, that has greater range and penetrative power than a plate missile, but with a similarly effective reaction behind the protective armour. As a rule of thumb, the penetration to be expected from an SFF is between 50 and 100 per cent of the warhead calibre, although this will decrease with range. Typically, SFF could not be expected to be effective much beyond 50 or 60 metres.

Despite the limitations outlined above for shaped and plate charges and SFF, they do remain useful as attack mechanisms in AT mines. The range restrictions are not prohibitive in a mine warfare context and the penetrations available are presently adequate for belly or side attack. Yet warhead technology can not stand still. Other than for powerful, blast effect, HE mines there is no reliable way of attacking heavy tank tracks and, until a way is discovered, there can be no really true FWA mine. Equally, armour improvements are being introduced to inhibit the effectiveness of existing modes of attack, which must be up-rated to meet such counter-measures. These and other counter-mine activities are about to be examined, to provide an appreciation of the hostile environment in which mines must function.

7

Counter-mine Warfare

Introduction

Terminology

THERE are a variety of terms met frequently in counter-mine warfare, which have similar, but different, meanings that can become confused or applied incorrectly. It will be useful to differentiate between them at this early stage. Neutralizing or disarming a mine can be achieved in several ways. Disarming is the procedure specified by a manufacturer to reverse the arming process and render the mine safe. It could, for example, be as simple as turning a lever from the ARMED position to the SAFE mark and inserting a safety pin to prevent its further movement. Neutralizing a mine is often a more complicated activity, that might involve, as a first step, disarming the mine. A search for anti-handling or anti-disturbance devices connected to the mine would be undertaken too. Generally, the presence of an anti-lift or handling device would prevent neutralization, as the mine should then be destroyed *in situ*, being too unstable to tamper with. Neutralization is achieved when the detonator or fuze is removed from the body of the mine and the device is incapable of operating as a whole. Sterilization, on the other hand, is a term implying that the internal mechanism has been locked in such a fashion that the mine is incapable of functioning. It may be placed in such a state by an extension of the disarming action, or be the outcome of an intended self-sterilization process. In electronically controlled mines, it may not be a mechanical interlock that prevents operation, but an electrical gate that is imposed or a complete battery drain that is effected. Whatever the means of sterilization, it is likely that there will be no external indication of the state of the mine. It is in such situations, when there is uncertainty over the safe or stable condition of a mine, that a technique known as pulling is used. This requires a length of cord or rope to be fixed to the mine, normally by means of a non-magnetic grappling hook. The rope is uncoiled to a safe distance, beyond the lethal range of the mine should it explode, and the mine is cautiously pulled over itself. If it fails to detonate after this disturbance, the mine is deemed safe for handling and can be removed from the vicinity for destruction or neutralization.

Operations to deal with more than one mine are specified as either breaching, clearance or recovery. Breaching a minefield has connotations of tactical necessity. It covers any method used to secure a route through a mined area, normally under operational conditions. The breach will be adequate to permit the passage of those troops and vehicles, which the immediate situation requires, and no more. It could be as narrow as the path required for men to pass in single file on a night fighting patrol, or comprise several parallel but separate routes each capable of transit by an MBT. Breaching could be achieved by hand under cover of darkness, by explosive means to obtain a rapid passage or by tank mounted ploughs and rollers under enemy fire. Clearance is an activity designed to remove all mines, booby traps and IEDs from a route or area. It can only be done by hand, carefully and slowly, to provide an absolute confidence that the area is clear. Naturally, this is an operation not to be attempted in the face of the enemy. Concentration is demanded from the clearance parties and time must be allowed for a thorough task to be completed safely. Whilst there is inherent in breaching a chance that some mines may not have been found or neutralized, this is usually an acceptable risk in war. Clearance on the other hand is a means of guaranteeing that no mines remain in that area. Typically, a clearance operation might be carried out on a major supply route to ensure that all verges, passing places, hide areas and refuelling points are free from danger and that landmines are not present below the road surface or hidden in culverts or under bridges. In a different context, the Argentinian minefields near Port Stanley and other centres of population on the Falkland Islands have been cleared by UK combat engineers, aided by pioneers and initially some Argentinian prisoners of war. This was a necessity to ensure the safety of civilians after cessation of hostilities. An interesting off-shoot of this activity is known as battlefield area clearance, also under way on the Falklands, and similarly undertaken by members of the Royal Engineers and Royal Pioneer Corps. It involves searching known battle areas for any dangerous or explosive material that remains after the fighting. Ammunition can be sorted for re-use on training, explosives will be collected and burned, unexploded shells and mortar bombs would be blown-up *in situ*, all to render the environment safe for the civil population and their livestock. Of course, much of this sort of clearance would be completed after any war, just as the final anti-mine operation, recovery, would also have to be effected. Recovery implies complete clearance of all dangerous items from a mined area, it normally refers to lifting mines laid by friendly forces, and is usually carried out with the aid of a minefield record. Equally, there is the inference that the mines recovered will be available for use elsewhere or be suitable for return to supply dumps and depots.

Responsibilities

Mines are a threat to every soldier in war, and, regrettably, to a much wider cross-section of the populace where terrorism or insurgency exists. The ever present danger from mines in a combat zone gives rise to the requirement for men of all arms and services to be able to recognize and disarm those devices, both enemy and friendly, most likely to be encountered. This may seem a tall order and an evidently heavy training load, but in an era of RDM and air delivered, area denial weapons no soldier should feel he will be safe from mines. It is important that any serviceman, finding himself in a mined area, has the confidence and knowledge to extricate himself by disarming those mines he can, and avoiding those he cannot. Thus, counter-mine warfare is not simply a responsibility of combat engineers. Their special responsibilities start in the training of other arms to challenge the mine and extend into the specific area of counter-measures. They are the ones who search for, detect and mark mines, plan and carry out breaching and undertake the clearance or recovery of minefields.

In peacetime, the onus for anti-terrorist operations is generally placed on the police and this includes dealing with insurgent IEDs and landmines. However, most nations have specially trained troops to support the police force in this work. Such military specialists may be from the combat engineer arm or, just as likely, from the ordnance services of the army, air force and navy. These men are trained in both the disposal of IEDs and in the vast range of conventional munitions used by their particular branch of the armed forces. The enormous number and variety of mines, shells, bullets and guided missiles that could be included in this latter classification are beyond human ability to remember in detail. For this reason an initiative has been taken by several NATO nations to form the Explosive Ordnance Disposal Technical Information Centre (EODTIC) in southern England. The Centre provides a focus for detailed information on a worldwide range of explosive munitions that the EOD specialists of the contributing nations may be called upon to deal with. Within an alliance such as NATO, where individual nations, each with its own armaments industry, procure often quite different weapons to achieve the same purpose, there is a genuine need for the soldiers of one member state to be able to neutralize or dispose of the munitions of the other states. This applies to every service, since army corps stand alongside each other in Central Europe, mixed nationality flotillas patrol the Atlantic, and reinforcing wings of fighter aircraft must operate from host airfields throughout the NATO area of responsibility. Accidents during training, terrorist acts, and operations in war can all give rise to the EOD operative having to face the dangers of an unexploded device or munition that he has never seen before. At last, EODTIC can offer the man in the field access to an enormous technical database and relevant, professional advice to aid him in his hazardous occupation. EODTIC points the way for other alliances, regional organisations or international federations. Just as much as NATO, they too have a requirement for comprehensive and up-to-the-minute information on material of an explosive nature, which can only be provided by a full-time dedicated team of interested and knowledgeable experts. The clearance of new-style naval mines, laid by unknown hands in the Suez Canal, and carried out by forces of different nations, plus the nightmarish flight of a Soviet missile into Finnish airspace near the northern tip of NATO are two recent incidents illustrating that the demand for EOD expertise can never be predictable. When EOD support is called upon, it is often in an emergency and time is inevitably short. The availability of high-quality, current technical information from EODTIC or the like may mean the difference between life and death, between normality and devastation. Those responsible for EOD, who do not have access to a centre such as EODTIC, must consider themselves at a disadvantage and should seriously contemplate the establishment of a similar focus.

Counter-measures

Anti-mine Protection

To reduce the physical effects of a mine attack, and to heighten psychological resistance to the threat of mines, it is possible to provide extra protection for men and vehicles. In the past this has often been an after-thought, being a reaction to mine casualties and intended to bolster morale. The results were usually cumbersome, inelegant and limited in effectiveness. New materials and modern design processes now permit mine-resistant clothing and vehicles to be provided at the outset. What is required is an appreciation of the threat and a determination to meet it. In the realm of personal protection, past attempts provide useful indicators to future possibilities. Early mine breaching parties found that a major contribution to casualties was the eye damage caused by even tiny particles of debris resulting from a mine explosion. The soldier may have been searching the ground and prodding carefully, laying flat on the ground and working at arms length, nevertheless, the sensitive pressure mine would somehow be activated. The force of the explosion would usually be in a vertical direction and the soldier would not be affected, other than by shock and a shower of earth, sand, stones or casing splinters. If eyes were unprotected then considerable injury could be caused to his eyesight. For this reason mine clearance goggles were introduced and remain in use to this day. The danger to sensitive eyes remains from any type of mine explosion and the more recent means of protecting them is to provide a full face visor, made from clear, see-through material such as Makralon. This type of protection is afforded to Royal Engineer (RE) Search Teams and Royal Army Ordnance Corps (RAOC) EOD specialists of the British Army, particularly in Northern Ireland. The head as a whole is particularly vulnerable in any event and increased defence is being provided by the replacement of old-fashioned, heavy steel helmets by lighter, better designed varieties manufactured from modern materials. Forces that have experienced recent combat are taking the lead in purchasing these light-weight helmets: the United States has already bought one million Kevlar helmets and UK forces are being re-equipped in a similar fashion. The new materials, which offer improved levels of protection yet lighter weight, are advanced ceramic, or composite armours. A composite material consists of a reinforcement fibre or different fibres contained within a cohesive substance, called the matrix. The fibres may be carbon, glass, Kevlar, boron or other strands that can withstand stress and provide mechanical strength. The matrix is usually a setting polymer, such as epoxy resin or polyester, that can provide structural support and environmental protection for the fibres. The fibre/matrix composition is also known as laminate armour. Laminates can be combined with ceramics (aluminium oxides), or ceramics with metals to provide sandwich armours. Up-to-date body armour normally consists of a laminate/ceramic sandwich. Armour technology now allows this bullet-proof vest or flak jacket type of protection to be optimized to defeat a specific threat, be it high velocity rifle fire or mine fragments. The armoured suits worn by EOD operatives are a result of advances in this sphere, and derivatives could find an application in mine breaching or clearance. There is a precedent for this, which arose at the end of World War II when mine clearance parties provided themselves with makeshift protective suits from motorcycle boots, padded flying trousers, leather jerkins and heavy duty gloves. Sandwich armour might also provide a suitable and comfortable style of mine-resistant boot. Early attempts to provide security for feet and legs depended upon spreading the weight of the man over such a large surface that the mine fuze would not respond to his ground pressure. Self-help devices were made from planks of wood and the issue version of the mine boot proved to be a large, clumsy pad — tiring to wear and difficult to walk on. Whilst such measures did help to prevent pressure mines activating, they increased the likelihood of fouling trip wires and offered no physical protection. A new, knee length boot made from laminate fabric with ceramic inserts to protect the sole, heel and calf is a feasible product now and would offer true mine-resistance. If the will is there to protect soldiers from mines, and other dangers, then existing technology can produce the means. Both Israel and the United States enforce a policy of personal protection through the provision of body armour to their general combat forces. The United Kingdom makes it available to specialists such as the SAS anti-terrorist units and EOD sections, or troops on duty in Northern Ireland. Perhaps this tendency will become more widespread, allowing SCICON's glimpse of the future in the form of Infantryman 2000 to take shape in reality. They visualize him operating in a Tactical Vest, which incorporates a harness for his packs and pouches on a protective armour base that can be up-armoured or selectively reinforced as the situation dictates. Protection from remotely delivered AP mines is given to the lower legs by a High Boot comprising rigid armoured soles and flexible armoured uppers. All of these proposals are technically feasible, albeit the operational requirement has yet to be recognized sufficiently clearly to permit their general introduction into the armed services.

There is just as much, probably more, to be done in the way of designing mine resistance into vehicles or adding extra protection to existing designs, than in the area of personnel protection. The very point of contact between the vehicle and the ground can be configured to improve its chance of survival. If a six wheel lay-out is used, then the loss of a wheel station in a mine explosion may not necessarily stop the vehicle, which still has five wheels to run on. Should the remaining wheels be fitted with run-flat tyres, this will enhance the chance of retaining mobility still further, since tyres punctured by blast and shrapnel will continue to support the vehicle's weight. There are a variety of types of track too, that can be chosen for tracked AFVs. The two principal options are those employing either a single link pin or a double pin design. Within these options, the dry pin form usually offers the lightest and cheapest solution, whereas the rubber-bushed pin increases the thickness and weight of the track. Thus the heaviest and most robust form is the rubber-bushed, double pin track, providing the toughest track for a pressure mine to defeat. Boat shaped hulls for vehicles have been considered as a defensive mechanism in the past, as this is a configuration which would deflect the blast of an exploding mine and cause plate charge projectiles to ricochet. The obvious disadvantage is the loss of space within the vehicle, unless the vehicle silhouette is raised to an unacceptable height. Nevertheless, one nation found it less hazardous to follow this route than retain standard, flat based vehicles: ARMSCOR produce a wide range of mine resistant, wheeled vehicles for the South African Defence Forces. The Buffel troop carrier is the best known of these, providing virtually total protection for the passengers from land mines, a claim substantiated in operations. The Samil range of vehicles also includes armoured horse transporters, ambulances and cargo carriers. Defence against the mine is provided by the V shaped body, raised well off the ground, and by isolating the crew and cargo from engine and fuel in an armoured compartment. Elsewhere, other thoughts on protective design have given rise to run-flat tyres, heavy mine proof tracks, explosion proof fuel tanks and polycarbonate glass capable of defeating blast and shrapnel. New armours also impinge upon the design process. The saving in weight offered by composites such as Kevlar is sometimes as great as 50 per cent over steel armour offering the same protection. Thus, for the same weight, a tank belly could be given up to twice the protective strength by substituting laminate for steel armour. There are regrettably, two disadvantages. Composite materials are decidedly more expensive than standard steel armours and the lack of rigidity in these laminates has created considerable difficulties in incorporating them into the structural framework of an AFV. However, armour can account for as little as 10 per cent of the price of an AFV. Consequently, increasing costs in this area, whilst enhancing survivability of the whole vehicle, would not show a dramatic rise in the total cost of the AFV. Equally, considerable advances have been made in the production of laminated and ceramic armours to permit their shaping and direct design into load-bearing, armoured structures. Thus, there is evident potential for a rigorous review of traditional design concepts to heighten intrinsic mine resistance. The next generation of vehicles may well reveal that this aspect has been given due consideration. In the meantime, those vehicles in service must be improved on an ad-hoc basis when the mine threat is greatest.

There are many examples, both historical and current, to illustrate the inadequacy of vehicle designs to meet the challenge of mines, resulting in temporary and makeshift protective arrangements. Sandbags were used in World War II on the floors of troop carrying vehicles or in the driver's cab, and under his seat; US soldiers used heavy rubber mats within APCs in Vietnam and UK forces have employed bolt-on, steel armour plates to protect landrovers in many counter-insurgency campaigns since 1945. Add-on, or appliqué, armour has returned to favour recently. Soviet BMPs in Afghanistan have been fitted with extra side armour; the Egyptian firm, Kader, have reinforced M113A2 APCs with all round, appliqué armour consisting of a composite and aluminium sandwich; and Israeli Merkava, M60 and Centurion MBTs have been seen with add-on reactive armour. This latter form of protection is marketed as Blazer explosive armour by Israel Military Industries. It is produced in bolt-on blocks, is custom-designed for each type of MBT, and is said to be compatible with all the external protrusions to be found on an MBT. Reactive armour is optimized to defeat HEAT warheads and is, therefore, of special interest as protection against shaped charge, belly attack mines or LAW based ORM. The specific design of Blazer is a commercial secret, but the concept of reactive armour is well known. It is a matrix of explosive and armour material, which explodes outwards the instant that an incoming, hollow charge jet penetrates its surface. This explosion disrupts the stream of hot gas, preventing penetration of the main armour below. Outside of an operational theatre there are, naturally, severe objections to carrying live explosive on an AFV exterior and reactive armour is only ever likely to be used in a hostile environment. Yet the flat, bolt-on boxes are ideally suited for fixing to the smooth belly of an AFV and could provide a very effective counter-measure to mines. Where external fixing of extra armour is unaccept-able, for reasons of cost, weight or impracticality, an internal option still exists. Sandbags and rubber matting were used in the past to limit behind-armour effects by trapping fragments, diffusing jets of hot gas or dispersing blast. The same can now be achieved with soft armours. These are low-weight, flexible blankets or liners made from laminates, such as Du Pont's Kevlar aramid fire. In addition to their deadening and disrupting effect on armour penetrators, these liners also offer resistance to radiation, chemicals and fire. It seems inevitable that composite liners will become a common feature of future AFVs, just as the modern, sandwich armours, of the Chobham or Ceralu type, will provide their main structural component. These developments in armour protection combine to suggest that the successful attack of foreseeable targets will provide an immense challenge for mine designers, even without the consideration of the mine counter-measures that follow.

Reconnaissance

The most effective way of countering mines is to avoid them. Mobile columns, intent on penetrating deeply into the rear areas of a defensive zone, will wish to by-pass enemy positions, obstacles and minefields in particular. Although any commander will be suspicious as his force advances, and allows itself to be deflected and diverted by minefields emplaced to do that very thing, he will be willing to accept this situation provided his combat intelligence is adequate. There can be no certainty in his knowledge of the enemy's dispositions or intentions, but his calculated risks will be based upon a professional assessment of the information provided by his reconnaissance assets. Depending upon the sophistication of the armed forces involved, there are a whole variety of reconnaissance means that can be employed to identify minefields. The recce patrol or armoured car section can use eyes, binoculars or image intensifiers to locate minefield fences or rows by day or night. ORMs and mines buried by hand can be very effectively camouflaged and concealed, only to be identified by a recce group when casualties are inflicted. But, of course, this is one of the ways in which they have traditionally obtained information, and scouts or point-men recognize that they tend to be in greater jeopardy than the remainder of the force, in order to protect that force. Since mechanical mine laying inevitably leaves tell-tale marks on the land, in the form of furrows or vehicle tracks, minefields laid in this way can be readily identified from the air. Helicopters can be an effective and rapid, if risky, way of locating these minefields. When more time is available, aerial photography is a reliable method of fixing the extent of minefields. The photographs can be issued directly to the troops who have to avoid, or in some cases breach, the minefield, or the information can be simply transferred on to battle maps for subsequent issue. In this age of high-resolution cameras carried in satellites or high-level transit, recce aircraft, there is no difficulty in recognizing enemy minefields well before they are reached, or even before hostilities actually commence, should they have been laid during a time of increased tension. Modern electro-optic techniques also make it possible to determine the location of concealed mines, or mines that have been in the ground for a considerable time. This is achieved using false colour, or IR film. Disturbed ground or vegetation is revealed in a readily visible minefield pattern. Airborne IR scanners can provide similar information, but with the additional benefit of almost real-time transmission of those details to the ground force headquarters. All of these reconnaissance facilities are useful in determining the limits of conventional, pattern minefields, however, the emergence of SM and RDM has introduced a new reconnaissance problem for mobile forces. The rapidity, with which these mines can be imposed, requires an unusually reactive and speedy response from any agency that encounters them, or observes them being laid. For it is very unlikely that it will be the well-trained, specialist recce troops that meet RDM initially, as the enemy using them will have chosen his target carefully to gain maximum effect and disruption from their unexpected arrival. Consequently, all troops must be prepared to recognize and report the presence of mines in a rapid and sensible fashion, preferably to a commonly agreed format. Mine consciousness, and the ability to relay information about mines or minefields, can no longer be the restricted province of combat engineers or recce forces. Mines are a common threat, to be dealt with on an all arms basis.

Detection

General observation and a brief reconnaissance can indicate that a minefield lies ahead. This basic information may be inadequate for the commander's needs and a more detailed examination of the potential obstacle may be called for. The most obvious reason why this is necessary is to remove any doubt over whether it is a real or phoney minefield. A closer look by an engineer reconnaissance party could determine that no mines have been laid, thus avoiding the need for detours and a radical change of plan. If mines are present, the force engineer commander needs to know what type they are, in what density and to what depth. These facts will permit a breaching operation to be planned that is specifically suited for that size and type of minefield, without risking scarce and expensive counter-measure equipment on an obstacle that does not warrant any greater expenditure of time and effort. Normally, the recce into the minefield will be carried out by combat engineers, probably at night if time permits and with protective fire available on demand. Its purpose will be to determine how the enemy has designed the minefield, how many rows there are, what types of mines and fuzes he has employed, over what depth. Naturally this is a lengthy procedure, not to say dangerous, and it represents the ideal. The situation may demand that a breach is undertaken, without preparation, from the line of march, using the mechanical and explosive means described below. This can be done using standard drills and assuming the enemy has a recognized method of laying his minefields. In making this choice the tactical commander will take a calculated risk on likely enemy reaction, their strength of covering fire, the suppressive fire his own forces can bring to bear in support of the breach and the damage to breaching equipment he can afford to absorb.

If time allows, there are a number of aids that engineer recce parties can utilize in their search for enemy mines. Some may be more applicable to mine detection outside of minefields, say in searching for mines in an urban area, but all deserve mention here. The earliest and most primitive, yet commonly used and enduring, method is prodding. Originating in World War I, developed to a high level during World War II, employed during 1982 in the Falklands Campaign, and even more recently by Soviet troops in Afghanistan, the use of a bayonet or specially designed aluminium prodder is often the most available and reliable means of locating mines. It is not a sharp, downward stabbing motion but a careful, angled push through the ground surface in a measured, deliberate manner to cover the whole front allocated to a particular soldier. This skill is something every soldier should be practised in, for none can be sure when they may require to use it under operational conditions. Dogs have been used as an alternative to detect mines in the past, usually when prodding or the use of mine detectors was not feasible. The dogs do get tired and distracted, just as their human colleagues do in this laborious, but nevertheless hazardous, endeavour. Dogs have been particularly valuable in checking railway lines, built-up areas, rocky ground and rubble for mines. In fields and meadows there are many more interesting scents to divert their attention from the task in hand.

Mine detectors, of course, have been the most important development to assist minefield recce, breaching or clearance parties. The first British sensing device was called the Polish detector, after the two Polish officers who had designed it. Early detectors were heavy and cumbersome, some being mounted on a two-wheel trolley, whilst others were worn on a harness, with a counter-balance weight behind the operator. Daunting devices such as the British X7 deep-buried mine detector and the No. 5, with a 6 foot wide search head, have given way to the current, standard issue No. 4c, which is lightweight and fully transistorized. Most nations produce detectors: GIAT make the DHPM1A in France. BETA of Israel produce the BMD-34, and Institute Dr Forster of West Germany have an international reputation for the quality and range of their detector products. The type of detector can be one of three basic models. The inductive bridge detector operates on the principle that a ferrous object will distort a primary magnetic field surrounding a coil containing alternating current. An oscillator, producing the current, the coil system, and an amplifier are held in balance at the start of a sweep. The distortion from a metallic mine or component will cause an imbalance, which is notified to the operator by a sound in his head-set or indicated on a dial. The regenerative type of detector indicates the presence of a secondary magnetic field. This secondary field is built-up in a metal object by the primary field emanating from the detector's search head. The third type of detector is very sensitive and is usually referred to as a mine locator. This device has a circuit that is finely tuned to be in balance with the local earth magnetic field. Thereafter, the presence of ferro-magnetic material will increase the density of the lines of force and place the detector into a state of imbalance, alerting the operator. These locators are most commonly used in the search for beach mines or unexploded bombs, and increasingly in anti-terrorist work. In addition to the standard, hand-held detector, versions have been mounted on vehicles. These can be linked to the vehicle's brakes, so that it is halted immediately a mine is detected. The United States have such a device, as do the Soviets in the form of the jeep mounted DIM detector and a similar device is positioned on their IPR engineer reconnaissance vehicle. It is also claimed that advanced mine detectors can be carried in helicopters, which, when coupled to a computerized display, can map out entire minefields. If true, this could be a useful addition to the rapid reconnaissance capability of a mobile force, but will be of limited value when plastic mines are in use or the specific type of mine has to be identified. To deal with plastic mines, non-metallic detectors have been introduced. Typical are the US AN/PRS-7 and United Scientific NMD-78, which rely for their effect upon detecting a change in the dielectric constant from that of the surrounding soil. Despite these advances, the only sure way of finding non-metallic mines is by hand and by prodding, as a consequence of the wide range of soil types that can be encountered with any number of solid objects contained within them.

Rudimentary Breaching

The use of hands, prodders and mine detectors is the basis of hand breaching. This is the oldest technique for effecting a breach and can be the slowest, but also the most thorough and effective. If time permits, if the soldiers are well trained and motivated, if cover is provided by night or smoke, and the enemy does not interfere, then hand breaching is an ideal choice. However, the skills to do it safely and the techniques to carry it out efficiently need to be practised. This not only applies to the combat engineers, for breaching is a combined arms task: infantry may have to infiltrate the minefield to eliminate enemy observation posts (OPs), machine gun nests or similar close protection; tanks will be positioned as over-watch, to provide covering fire for the breaching party should a counter-attack be launched by the enemy; artillery OPs would be close by to offer similar protection, or to fire smoke cover, or to respond with counter-battery fire to enemy artillery firing at the breach. Thus to be effective, hand breaching operations have to be rehearsed on training exercises and well co-ordinated on operations. Sometimes, there are no alternatives to hand breaching, as equipment may not be available or conditions could demand a silent breach. It is more likely that a commander is not able to accept the time required for a hand breach in his plan, or is unwilling to accept the casualties that could be inflicted on breaching parties exposed in open minefields. There are then a variety of possible improvisations that could be tried. Allied troops in Italy during World War II were said to have herded flocks of sheep through German minefields in an attempt to clear paths through. On the Eastern Front, Russian troops were marched through minefields at the point of a gun, apparently accepting the lower chance of injury from a mine than the certainty of death from a bullet. Similar, callous disregard for life and limb was displayed by the Viet Cong who forced civilians to precede them through perimeter defence minefields on to American positions. These latter tactics are hardly to be recommended or adopted by anybody other than the most ruthless or fanatical of forces. An alternative, impromptu approach would be to attempt to drive through a minefield as soon as it is encountered. This is known as bulling or bouncing the obstacle, and historical precedent would suggest that this is a practice to be avoided. During November 1942, a regiment of British light tanks attempted to assault through a German minefield in North Africa. The entire force of 40 tanks was immobilized or destroyed. Israeli forces were similarly halted at Um Katef and delayed at Khan Yunis in their assaults on Arab positions. The need to maintain momentum in the advance or comply with a commander's insistent demands for progress could lead to an attempted bounce crossing of a minefield, but it is hardly a tactic to be considered as a general option.

Mechanical Counter-measures

Yet the urgency of the situation and the desire to keep the tempo of operations at a high level may compel a tactical commander to take unwelcome risks or accept high casualties by bulling through a minefield, if there is no realistic option. To provide a mechanized force with an alternative to this possibility, mechanical counter-measures have been developed. The great number of mines laid by the Afrika Korps in the western deserts presented a major problem to British forces, and their attempts to maintain mobility despite German minefields led to the introduction of the flail tank. The flail was designed by a South African engineer serving with the Allied forces, a Major A. S. du Toit. He proposed that a rotating drum be mounted across the front of a tank. As the drum turned, driven by an auxiliary motor or the vehicle engine, lengths of chain attached to it would be whipped through the air to beat a path ahead of the tank. The heavy chains would have sufficient energy to detonate or destroy any mines they hammered into. Initially fitted to obsolescent Matildas, the flails were eventually fitted to Grant and Sherman chassis. By the time they were mounted on these Shermans, the flails had become well-developed, counter-mine equipments and had been adopted for general service under the specific name Sherman Crab. Also fielded in alternative forms such as the Baron and the Scorpion, the flail concept saw repeated use in Allied hands during World War II, especially as part of the specialized 79th Armoured Division during the Normandy landings and in the subsequent break-out and pursuit. After World War II, the flail lost favour and was phased out of service by most nations. It does have several failings, which could account for this. The flail and its chains are necessarily heavy and large items that increase the weight, height and length of the carrier, normally a tank. In operation, the tank has to drive slowly to ensure that the flail beats an even path. When operating, the flail generates considerable noise and dust, both of which are exacerbated as mines detonate. Thus, flailing is a noisy, slow and obvious way of effecting a breach. Even when parked, or simply moving from place to place, the flail/tank combination is a large and unwieldy item, very difficult to conceal and transport. The flail could also be defeated by DI fused mines and variations in ground level, such as hollows or shallow ditches, could cause the chains to miss the surface, leaving mines untouched. Since 1945, most attention has been paid to mechanical counter-measures other than the flail, although they were used by the Syrians to breach Israeli defences on the Golan Heights in 1973. More recently, an interesting development of the flail concept has been undertaken in Great Britain by a company called Aardvark. They offer an advanced flail, with a variety of chain ends optimized for the likely mine and selected role. It can be used in a rapid breaching situation or on a deliberate clearance operation, and on a variety of surfaces or terrain, from airfield runways to scrub-covered hillsides. Attention to detail has overcome many of the previous objections. Although its optimum speed of operation is less than 3 miles per hour, it can claim 100 per cent success in clearance of mines with a diameter of 3 inches or more at this velocity. Calculations show that every square inch in front of the vehicle is beaten at least twice to achieve this level of performance. The design also incorporates a contouring device to follow the shape of the ground and a blast deflection plate between the flail and the prime mover. In addition to diverting the hazardous products of an explosion, the plate prevents mines being flicked below the vehicle. Such protection permits a variety of vehicles to be used as the carrier for the Aardvark flail, from 4-ton trucks through wheeled tractors to MBTs. When correctly operated, the device will breach a cleared lane through any type of patterned minefield, across an area where SM or RDM have been laid or through a belt of airfield or area denial weapons. Flails were shown to be effective mine clearers between 1942 and 1945, when they were successfully used against pressure activated mines in a variety of operational theatres. The introduction of modern influence fuzes, anti-disturbance mines and devices that detonate in a random fashion has made counter-mine warfare more dangerous. Perhaps the brutal simplicity of a flail can provide the answer to dealing with this complex range of sophisticated mines. Elsewhere in Western Europe, it is known that a Franco-German development resulted in a flail being fitted to an M48 tank chassis. Equally, Krupp MaK are thought to be examining the feasibility of producing a flail-equipped mine clearing vehicle, also based on an M48 vehicle chassis. It appears that this battle-proven mine counter-measure device may soon be back in favour amongst NATO nations.

A much more popular solution to mechanical mine clearance has been the anti-mine roller. In the era of pressure fuzed mines, these heavy, crushing rollers proved their worth. Originally used during World War II, the rollers have been produced in a variety of forms. The smallest version was probably the Rodent. This equipment consisted of small rollers pushed aread of the miniscule tracked vehicle known as the Weasel. Rodent was specifically designed to clear routes of the German Schu mine, at which it was quite effective, but provided no match for any of the heavier AT mines. To withstand the explosive force of the standard AT mine, rollers are usually very rugged and very weighty. The roller assembly in use at present by American forces is close on 10 tons, but even this pales when compared to some earlier proposals. To provide a completely cleared route, it was thought that full width rollers would be a potential solution. In the United States, these were known as Larraping Lou and High Herman, whilst the United Kingdom developed T10 — a front and rear, full width roller combination. The enormous weight, bulk and unwieldiness of these monstrosities proved to be completely impractical and steered future development towards purely track-width rollers. Such rollers were used effectively in Vietnam by US mechanized troops, despite the inability of this particular counter-measure to deal with DI fuzed mines. Another danger is that from tilt-fuze or other belly attack devices, which may be missed between the tracks. A partial solution has been to hang a heavy chain between the rollers to snatch tilt rods and detonate their charges before the pusher-vehicle passes over them. Alternatives to this have been to drape a curtain of chains between the rollers or to suspend a chain link mat in front of the tank's belly. Possibly the best known roller system is the PT 54/55 assembly available to Warsaw Pact tank forces. The rollers are constructed in a typical manner from several heavy discs aligned side by side. This allows individual discs to be replaced as they become damaged by exploding mines, rather than removing the entire roller. As well known as the Soviet PT 54/55 device is, it owes much of its recognition to the length of time it has been in service. The most modern counter-mine roller is that available from Urdan RKM of Israel. Called the Mine Clearing Roller System (MCRS), it can be adapted for fitting on a wide range of MBT, including M-60, Centurion, Chieftain, AMX-30 and Leopard. A specifically configured adaptor is shaped to fit the front glacis plate of each type of MBT. Two men can then fit the MCRS to the adapted tank within 15 minutes using a standard hoist. The assembly can be released much more quickly, if the situation demands. A manual disconnection can be achieved in 30 seconds, but for those occasions when the crew could be in jeopardy, an instantaneous release can be effected remotely from within the tank. This is valuable when the tank is isolated in a minefield and cannot proceed, perhaps because the rollers have been destroyed or heavy fire is endangering the vehicle, and a rapid withdrawal is essential. This remote release is achieved by blowing-out the retaining pins with small explosive charges that neither damage the vehicle nor roller assembly. The roller banks are designed to absorb the shock of an explosion rather than resist them, by having a vertical articulation of about 6 inches. Most of the mine's energy is dissipated by this recoil, the rest is conveyed to the pushing tank or converted into plastic deformation of the system. Although rollers can be damaged by SI fuzed mines and the parent vehicle attacked by DI fuzed devices, they continue to be deployed by forces with considerable experience of recent combat. They cannot be discounted as a viable counter-measure and, indeed, are being considered as a component of the future, remote-controlled, mine-clearing vehicle under development by the US Army Tank Automotive Command. Based upon a modified M60 chassis, the vehicle is referred to as the Robotic Obstacle Breaching Assault Tank (ROBAT). Sporting a top-mounted pod containing a rocket-propelled, explosive clearing hose and a rear-mounted, automatic marking system, the tank is also fitted with track-width rollers. These can be used initially to locate the forward row of enemy mines, or after the explosive hose has been deployed and detonated, to ensure the breach is clear of mines. The whole sequence of operation, including steering and firing of the hose, can be controlled by a distant operator, remote and safe from the effects of mines and other enemy fire directed at the vehicle. This development represents a novel and systematic approach to minefield breaching, bringing together proven mechanical and explosive counter-measures with new initiatives in breach marking and crew safety. It deserves to be successful, and provides a useful pointer to the way ahead for other nations intent on improving their counter-mine capability.

Another durable, mechanical counter-measure to mines has been the dozer blade. Armoured bulldozers were used in World War II to overcome obstacles, and continued to be used on Britain's beaches after hostilities to clear them of anti-invasion mines. Armoured tractors are still in UK service and have been used to remove barricades in Northern Ireland. Such vehicles could be used to clear SM from firm surfaces in the future, as could the Combat Engineer Tractor (CET). This is an armoured, specialist, engineer vehicle equipped with a versatile bucket that is wider than the tracks and is quite capable of dozing away surface-laid mines. The self-entrenchment device fitted to Soviet T64 and T72 tanks can sweep mines away from the area between their tracks, and other states produce full width dozer blades for some of their tanks that can be employed in a similar way. Israel Military Industries offer a tank dozer blade capable of being fitted to virtually any MBT, which can skim the surface to remove SM or rip down several inches to search for shallow buried mines. This is no doubt very similar to the Russian BTU, full width, tank dozer blade. The dozing ability of the blade fitted to the Soviet IMR engineer tractor is much better than any of these tank attachments could ever be, just as a civilian earthmover would out-perform any of these military improvisations. For this reason an add-on armour kit for bulldozers has been developed to protect the operator and machine when engaged on hazardous duties. Obtainable from Israel Military Industries, the kit provides an armoured, air conditioned cab plus armour plating for the engine and hydraulic system. Despite their efficiency in moving large quantities of soil, unearthing all the mines present, and removing the material, dozers and blades are best used in clearance operations when more time is generally available and enemy hindrance is less likely. For breaching tasks in the face of the enemy, a faster more survivable means is required. This is available in the form of the mine plough.

Early versions of the modern plough appeared in the Allied inventory during World War II. The Bullshorn plough was fitted to the Churchill tank and another version, the Jefferis Plough, was a product of the creative mind of Millis Jefferis whilst employed at that source of many inventive military devices: "Winston Churchill's Toyshop". Many types of full and track-width counter-mine plough have been examined since. One that has seen long service is the Soviet KMT4 plough. The Israeli forces have used their Ramta plough on active service, and the fearsome looking mine ploughs fitted to the US Marine Corps Landing Vehicle Tracked (LVT) were also used regularly under operational conditions in Vietnam. The principle of the mine plough is to comb through the surface of the ground with tines, or teeth, sufficiently close together to lift any mine to the surface, where it is pushed aside by the moldboard, or blade, to which the protruding tines are fixed. Skids attached to the inside of each, independent plough maintain the tines at a proper scarifying depth to engage and filter the mines to the surface. As with rollers, the area between track-width ploughs is protected by a heavy drag chain to defeat tilt-fuzed mines. The whole assembly can be controlled hydraulically, or by a simpler but less responsive screw-mechanism, from under the protection of the main armour of the tank. Because of the tractive effort required to push these ploughs through the ground, they are inevitably fitted to MBT. This makes tactical sense too, since the plough-equipped, gun tanks can be up forward with the advance elements, those troops most likely to encounter minefields first. When mines are discovered, the plough tanks take the lead. Being well-armoured they can accept considerable punishment from enemy fire and respond with their own main armament, machine guns and protective smoke dischargers. This ability to plough and shoot has proven its worth to Israeli forces under active service conditons. Fitted to M60 and Centurion tanks, the Ramta Track Width Mine Plough (TWMP) made by Israel Aircraft Industries is claimed to be reliable and simple to operate, in addition to being lightweight, high-strength and quickly installed. The British Army has recognized the effectiveness of the mine plough and has equipped its armoured engineer vehicles with the Pearson Engineering Mine Plough (EMP). Specifically designed for mounting on Chieftain Armoured Vehicle Launched Bridge (AVLB) bridgelayers and Centurion Armoured Vehicle Royal Engineers (AVRE) demolition gun tanks, the Pearson device is the most modern development of the plough anywhere in the world. Two versions are available, the EMP has 7 tines per plough and the Pearson TWMP has only 5 tines. The latter could be attached to non-engineer vehicles for more rapid, but less thorough, ploughing than is possible with the former. The EMP has given British forces a unique capability on NATO's Central Front, a fact recognized by their Canadian and American allies. Both of these nations have begun evaluation of the Ramta and Pearson ploughs, with a view to equipping their Leopard 1 and M1 Abrams MBTs with the most suitable contender. The Pearson EMP, being the more modern assembly, has been able to incorporate some novel features that have been absent on previous ploughs. In this age of SM and RDM, a valuable accessory is the hard-surface device, which attaches on to the tines. When so attached, the full-width, angled plates act as a mini-dozer blade, pushing surface laid mines to either side of the vehicle. This is particularly useful on tracks, roads, bridges, autobahns, runways or taxiways. In normal operation, the tines will clear AT mines down to a depth of almost 9 inches at speeds of 3 to 6 miles per hour, leaving an uncleared centre lane of just over 3 feet. This is considerably narrower than the uncleared path left by similar ploughs and usefully permits the breach to be used by a variety of vehicles, all smaller than MBTs, such as light reconnaissance tanks, APCs and wheeled supply vehicles. The speed of breaching is important because the slower a vehicle operates, the longer it remains exposed and vulnerable in the mined area. This is probably the greatest disadvantage of the interesting Soviet KMT-5 plough and roller combination. It is thought that the Warsaw Pact forces would use the KMT-5 once a minefield had been located by recce forces. Initially, only the roller would be lowered to advance into the mined area and to identify where the first mines were laid. Once this row was determined, the rollers would be raised and the plough then lowered into the ground to begin the clearance of the mines. Although an excellent idea, the great weight of the rollers and ploughs, plus the extra strain of ploughing, place a high demand on the parent MBT with the result that the breach is effected very slowly. At this snail's pace, the breaching tanks, and the vehicles waiting behind to use the breach, are extremely susceptible to the defender's fire. It is likely that this accounts for the fact that no other nations have attempted to copy the plough/roller combination concept as a viable counter-measure. Nor has anybody, up to the present, pursued the full-width mine plough (FWMP) option. This is now receiving attention in 2 areas. A current equipment is the FWMP produced by Israel Military Industries for attachment to powerful, tracked bulldozers such as the Caterpillar D9. Utilizing the inherent pushing power specifically designed into these heavy earthmovers, an FWMP is entirely feasible. Nevertheless, the vulnerability of bulldozers on the battlefield, despite add-on armour, suggests that this equipment has a greater contribution to make in clearance rather than breaching operations. The control system used to ensure that the plough follows the ground surface accurately is especially vulnerable to hostile action, depending as it does on forward mounted sensors. Perhaps an adaptation of the dozer FWMP would be useful in clearing airfield denial weapons, as this could be achieved both safely, by remote control, and efficiently, as a result of the automatic, contour following, plough control system. For the future, a very advanced concept is being developed by the United States in the form of the Counter Obstacle Vehicle (COV). This will be a powerful, combat engineer vehicle capable of dealing with a wide cross-section of battlefield obstacles such as AT ditches, road craters, tree blow-down, urban rubble and minefields. For this last task, the COV will be fitted with a combined mine plough/dozer blade that will clear a mine free path some 18 feet wide. If development proceeds to plan, and the COV meets its exacting specification, it will be the most functional and adaptable engineer vehicle in the world, representing a major advance in the mechanical mine counter-measure capability area.

Explosive Counter-measures

The origin of explosive methods of countering mines could be traced back to the days of true counter-mining, when defending forces would sink shafts and dig tunnels to trace and undermine the very tunnels that their enemies were digging towards them with the original aim of blowing the fortifications to pieces. It was a great dread among the soldier-miners of the American Civil War and World War I that their land mine galleries would be discovered by the enemy, who in turn would tunnel below them, exploding a massive charge in an ambush that could bury them alive. The use of explosives to clear routes through AP and AT minefields has a more recent starting point. As with many of the other counter-measures, the initial effort was a consequence of the operational necessities arising in World War II. Many extraordinary devices were proposed, developed and given limited employment in the field. The Snake consisted of a series of 3 inch diameter metal pipes, filled with explosive and towed behind a Sherman tank. At the minefield edge, the pipes would be repeatedly coupled together then pushed into the minefield by the tank, until the long run of explosive tubing could be pushed no further. This maximum was normally considered to be about 400 feet. After withdrawing a safe distance, the operators would detonate the length of pipe in an attempt to destroy or activate all those mines lying close to it. In effect, the Snake was a large Bangalore Torpedo and whilst the Bangalore remains in service with various nations, the Snake has virtually disappeared. Its only obvious descendant is the US M-157 mine clearing charge. This comprises some 80 sections of 5 feet long, twin section, explosive pipe. It is a very heavy and cumbersome kit, weighing almost 6 tons and would take 4 men over 4 hours to fit together. Having been assembled, section to section, at the edge of the minefield it is pushed on to the field by a heavy tracked vehicle, such as a tank or bulldozer. The tubes are detonated by firing heavy calibre, machine gun bullets at the impact fuse on the nearest pipe section. Designed to clear SI, pressure-fuzed mines over a width of 20 feet along its entire length, the kit is an effective, if slow and logistically demanding, mine clearance device. An additional disadvantage, that severely restricts its operational utility, is vulnerability — of the assembly team, the explosive tubes and the pusher vehicle. It is not an assault weapon. The smaller, man-portable Bangalore Torpedo is available to many forces, still being manufactured in the United States, Singapore, Israel and the Soviet Union. Each tube is 4 or 5 feet long, holding approximately 10 pounds of high explosive (HE). The tubes are screwed together to form a length that can continue to be pushed by one or two men into the minefield, where it is detonated to clear a path wide enough for men to pass in single file. Normally, up to 4 tubes can be man-handled so that on each detonation a path 20 feet long can be cleared. This is hardly a rapid means of breaching, and several attempts must be made by exposed, unprotected troops to clear a path through even the narrowest of protective minefields. To alleviate the tactical problems arising from the vulnerability of the teams and the length of time needed to effect a breach with Bangalore and M-157 type counter-measures, faster explosive methods of breaching have been sought.

The use of artillery or air delivered bombs to smash a route through a minefield has been considered. Practical difficulties have been encountered to suggest that neither of these methods are particularly suitable. Firstly, there is the problem of accuracy and dispersion. This is particularly true for bombs, which are an area weapon, although precision guided or laser directed munitions do improve the regularity of the impact pattern required to ensure that an area or route has been completely cleared. Tube artillery can be more accurate through the use of Forward Observation Officers (FOOs) to adjust the fall of shot, whilst multi-barrel rocket launchers and surface to surface missiles suffer from the same lack of consistency on target as free fall bombs. Lack of surprise is a further disadvantage, since it will be quite obvious to a defender that a heavy barrage or bomber attack on to a mined area is a prelude to an attempted breach of that minefield. There is also the question of logistics. A massive quantity of shells or bombs are needed to saturate the area of ground required for a breach, and their delivery will commit scarce artillery pieces and aircraft for a considerable time. It could be argued that this expenditure of ordnance would be far more effective if directly employed against the defenders, during or prior to a mechanical breaching operation. However, the greatest objection to a disruptive breach by explosive munitions is the state of the ground after the attack. Bomb craters and shell holes in close proximity do not amount to an easy ride, even for the most agile tracked vehicles. The pock-marked surface of the cleared lane could be so restrictive to movement that it is as great an obstacle to mechanized forces as the original minefield, requiring quite some effort from engineer plant equipment to restore the ground to a passable state. For these reasons, the breaching of minefields by bomb or shell is not favoured, with the notable exception of the Soviet forces. It appears to be an option they will consider for assault breaching, possibly because of the weight of artillery fire available to Soviet formations and their desire to continue the momentum of advance at almost any cost, and it is certainly a possibility that can not be ignored.

A much more practical mine counter-measure is the flexible explosive hose. This takes many forms and can vary from man-portable versions to those carried on AFVs, from rocket-propelled models, which precede a breach, to towed versions, that widen an initial breach. The first explosive hose to be used on operations was probably the Conger, a British weapon used at Calais in World War II. It consisted of a rocket-propelled hose, filled with nitro-glycerine, that exploded after contact with the ground. This is the basic concept that has been followed and improved upon ever since. The principle of operation being that all mines in the immediate vicinity of the explosion will be destroyed, whilst those SI, pressure-fuzed mines close at hand will be activated by the overpressure from the emanating shock waves. The resulting furrow, depending upon the size of the hose, will be wide enough for men to pass through safely in single file or for a vehicle to move forward with one track in the cleared channel.

For non-mechanized forces a variety of ground mounted rocket hoses were developed. A very simple device is the Bundeswehr's mine clearing rope, which consists of an 80-metre strand of toughened detonator cord, along which small packages of HE are attached at regular intervals. Pulled from its carrying box by a small rocket, the rope clears a footpath through AP mines some 70 metres long. Another German product is the mine clearing ladder, manufactured by Comet of Bremerhaven. Three parallel lines are separated by wooden spacers to give the impression of a rope ladder. Packages of plastic explosives are mounted every 25 centimetres along the length of the three lines and coupled by detonating cord to clear a route just less than 1 metre wide for approximately 50 metres. A more powerful rocket is employed, with stabilizing fins and twin towing wires to provide a predictable landing position for the ladder, which is anchored at its base point by two brake springs and earth spikes. The ladder charge is initiated after full extension by a 2-second delay, detonator switch, allowing the ladder time to settle on the ground before exploding. A very useful, non-explosive version is also available to permit repeated practice firings to take place during training or on field exercises. The live version weighs about 100 kilograms and can be mounted on skids for ease of transport to the edge of the minefield. Japan too produces a modern clearance device. This is Nissan's Type 70 line charge, which has been optimized for the destruction of AP mines. Its British equivalent, the Baby Viper is now obsolescent, although experience of the Falklands campaign has resurrected interest in this all arms weapon, capable of breaching a 140-metre path through an AP minefield. US forces also have dismounted clearance hoses. The MIAI projected charge is reported to breach a track over 2 metres wide and 50 metres long, whilst the M173 can clear 4 metres by 70 metres. To achieve this the M173 projects a total of almost 700 kilograms of explosive, contained in 800 interconnected segments. The extreme weight of the whole device necessitates its carriage in a specially designed, boat-shaped sledge, towed behind an AFV. The fibre glass sledge can float, giving an unusual, possibly unique, capability in that the kit could be used to breach minefields astride the bank of a river or canal, or on a beach. However, its normal mode of operation is to be towed to the edge of the area where the breach is required. The towing vehicle then positions the sledge accurately, and the crew can unhook it electrically from within the protection of the AFV armour. Withdrawing safely to cover, the towing crew are able to undertake the entire launch and detonation sequence remotely and securely by means of an 80 metre extension cable.

More advanced explosive hose systems are now available, mounted on vehicles or trailers, to provide a greater depth of breach and much quicker response times. For example, the Russian ground forces have the UR-67, twin rail explosive clearance system plus the improved UR-77 version, whilst the US Marine Corps have developed the M58A1. This latter device is a rocket projected hose charge, transported on a two-wheel trailer, and command detonated from the towing AFV. It is reminiscent of the better known and widely used Giant Viper system, produced by Royal Ordnance in Great Britain. The major component of Giant Viper is a 230-metre length of aluminized plastic explosive in a terylene/nylon hose. It is carried on a high mobility trailer that can be towed into action behind most AFVs and APCs, and delivered close to the breach site by any 4 tonne wheeled vehicle. Eight rocket motors in a circular configuration propel the heavy hose out to a distance of about 300 metres. Three parachutes then act in the arresting mode to straighten the hose in flight, to decelerate the hose on to the breach and to activate the detonator mechanism. Many tactical advantages accrue from the use of Giant Viper. After preparation of the kit in a hide area, it is driven forward but no closer than 100 metres to the edge of the minefield. Within 3 minutes, the hose is ready for firing from within the protection of the towing vehicle, yet all the time the vehicle's main armament is available to provide its own protective fire from a position well away from the dangerous killing ground close to the minefield. Having detonated, the hose will have cleared all AT and AP blast susceptible mines to a width of 7 metres and over a distance in excess of 180 metres. For minefields greater in depth than this the Tandem Firing Concept is used, whereby 2 Giant Viper trailers are hitched, one behind the other, to an MBT. The rear Giant Viper is fired from outside the minefield as in normal practice and is then jettisoned.

The tank proceeds into the minefield with the remaining trailer, along the breach it has just effected, to a point where the final hose is fired. In this manner, minefields approaching 400 metres deep can be breached in a matter of minutes. Thus, surprise is gained and the momentum of the assault is maintained. Equally, the rapidity and simplicity of the operation allows it to be carried out under the cover of darkness or behind the protection of a smoke screen or artillery concentration. Giant Viper is, therefore, an important element in the assault breaching capability of any mobile force and its availability in non-explosive training versions allows troops to become truly competent in its rapid employment. The utility of rocket propelled clearance hose has been proven and recognized world-wide, so much so that it is to form an integral part of the US Army's ROBAT concept vehicle.

An alternative use for flexible charges is to widen the initial breach after the first successful passage of a breaching vehicle. This idea too was conceived during World War II, when the Tapeworm was developed. The explosive hose in this case was dispensed from a trailer behind the lead vehicle. A similar device, the Boase Carpet comprising twin 3-inch explosive filled pipes, was used after D Day to clear routes for wheeled vehicles. A modern equivalent is CLEWP, the Israeli Military Industries Cleared Lane Explosive Widening and Proofing system. Reminiscent of a string of sausages, a 150 metres long line of separate but interconnected explosive charges are fed from a box mounted on the rear of a tank fitted with ploughs or rollers. The lid of the box is ejected to act as an anchor for the string of charges and the box itself is jettisoned at the end of the breach. Moving to a safe distance, the crew command detonate the charges, which ensure that the area between the plough furrows or roller tracks is completely cleared of mines. This allows the smaller, but equally essential, vehicles of the combat group to follow MBTs through the breach safely. An additional explosive method of widening a breach could be afforded by the use of liquid explosive. One such compound is Astrolite, manufactured by the Explosives Corporation of America. This could be spread from a bowser towed by the original breaching vehicle and detonated subsequently to ensure that any missed mines are destroyed. Interestingly, a liquid explosive could be viewed either as a land mine waiting for a target, or as a counter-measure to attack conventional mines.

The most modern explosive method of breaching is by fuel air explosive, abbreviated to FAE or FAX. This depends for its effect upon the formation of a heavy cloud of ethylene vapour, or similarly volatile charge, above the surface of the planned area of the breach. An ignition device detonates the suspension sending out pressure waves to destroy or actuate all mines in the local vicinity. FAE was used successfully by US forces in Vietnam, where it was delivered by parachute-retarded bombs dropped from helicopters. More recently, the US Army has developed the Surface Launched Unit (SLUFAE). Based on an M548 tracked cargo carrier, the 30 tube armoured launch unit can fire its 40 kilogram fuel air rockets individually or in a prolonged ripple. The maximum breach produced is almost 250 metres long by 10 metres wide, and this can be obtained at ranges from 300 metres to 1000 metres. It is a very effective and responsive stand-off breaching device, although it is necessarily expensive and logistically burdensome. Its availability on the battlefield will, therefore be limited, but its armoured protection and good mobility will allow it to be deployed quickly and safely to those points where it is required. A less sophisticated rocket FAE system has recently been brought on to the world market and offered for sale by the Chinese defence industry. Details have only been released to potential buyers, but it is known that the system is unarmoured and mounted on a wheeled chassis. The fact that the Chinese have an FAE mine counter-measure weapon offers a strong indication that the Soviet forces may have a similar capability. Undoubtedly, the Russian armaments industry could produce such a counter-mine device, and given the high level of interest in mine warfare amongst the Soviet military it is most unlikely that this system has been ignored by them. But the first modern FAE system to be introduced purely for counter-mine operations is likely to be the Catapult Launched FAE (CATFAE). This is under development by the FMC Corporation of Minneapolis for the US Marine Corps. They are seeking a device to be fitted to the LVT amphibian, that will allow beach assault forces to breach minefields at landing points. The CATFAE can be fired from offshore as the LVT approaches the beach and the requirement is to effect a breach in less than a minute. Honeywell Defence Systems Division are producing the FAE round itself, forming an integral part of the total system comprising fire control, sensors, launcher and vehicle interface equipment.

Of course, the most powerful explosive device is the nuclear weapon. The present levels of knowledge and capability in the design of nuclear-devices make it entirely feasible to develop a tactical weapon specifically for mine clearance. What form this might take is unknown, since only detailed analysis would reveal if the preferred solution would be to destroy or neutralize mines through any or all of the blast, heat or radiation effects of a nuclear explosion. No matter how effective this concept might prove to be as a mine counter-measure, it does suffer from the major limitation that its employment will be severely curtailed. In the majority of situations its use will be entirely unacceptable and its utility will be very restricted. Undoubtedly, this consideration has prevented such devices from being pursued or reported upon and reliance has continued to be placed in conventional explosives for minefield breaching.

Magnetic Deception

Many second generation belly attack mines have a sensor system based upon the principle of magnetic influence detection. This is also the most likely form of sensor to be found in SM or RDM. The magnetic influence fuze will be tuned to respond to a fairly narrow range of electromagnetic disturbance, typically that generated by its primary target, the enemy's MBT. It is clear that most counter-measures discussed so far will not be effective against magnetic influence fuzed mines, particularly those that have been buried. Thus, a requirement exists for a counter-measure to this type of mine. Some approaches are to minimize the magnetic signature of a vehicle by design, or alter the signature through magnetic coils, or attempt to remove it by demagnetizing the vehicle. All of these will work to a limited extent, but the electro-magnetic field is eventually built-up around the AFV or MBT, as the large piece of metallic equipment cuts through the earth's field. Unlike a large warship, which can accommodate the necessary equipment, it is not feasible to degauss an armoured vehicle and an alternative solution has to be found. The most promising development so far has been the Vehicle Magnetic Signature Duplicator (VEMASID). This compact, vehicle mounted equipment consists of an electro-magnetic coil and electronics module, feeding off the vehicle's electrical generator and battery. The coil can be fixed to a variety of combat vehicles in several ways: within the flotation screen of an APC, around the turret of a light tank or above the glacis plate of MBTs. Once energized, the coil duplicates the specific signature of the parent vehicle and projects it forward of the vehicle. Magnetic influence fuzes are deceived by this false image and detonate harmlessly ahead of the AFV. The distance in front of the vehicle at which mines will explode is a function of vehicle speed and the delay programmed into the mine fuze, but an initiation some 5 or 6 metres in advance of the AFV would not be abnormal. Being unobtrusive, with little logistic penalty, VEMASID is an important and acceptable addition to the existing range of counter-mine weapons in the US inventory.

Additional Options

The major counter-measure systems have been discussed above, but considerable inventiveness has been displayed over the years in examining and producing many other alternative methods. The Hippo was a high pressure pump mounted on an armour plated, 10-ton, tracked chassis. It was capable of delivering a powerful jet of water at up to 120 psi pressure. Taking water directly from the sea, Hippo was used extensively on Britain's beaches after World War II to clear them of the mines laid to inhibit invasion of the accessible coastline. Compressed air has also been used to expose mines as a means of detection, and this could have a future application too, along with jet efflux machines, in the clearance of SM and RDM from the paths of vehicles. Another proposal has been to bridge mined areas with protective barriers, such as quick setting foams, that would prevent pressure mines from actuating. In the future, helicopter mounted systems could have a part to play, perhaps towing grapples or fine mesh nets to remove SM, or rapidly dispensing explosive clearance devices over patterned minefields ahead of counter-stroke forces. At the very edge of technology is the further possibility that high energy transfer systems, for example particle beam generators, could be used to destroy mines accurately and effectively. For the present, the existing wide range of counter-measures available provides an adequate mix of counter-mine systems to meet most of the threats presented by current mines.

Breach Marking

Manual Methods

Experience gained in World War II suggested to many nations that once a breach had been made through a mined area, it was important to mark it clearly and securely. To cope with the extensive foot, wheeled and tracked traffic that large formations generated, the minefield gaps or lanes were heavily fenced. Along the side fences, white fabric tape would be laced and the fence posts would be signed with red and white marker plates and topped with lamps. Originally, the lights were simple hurricane oil lamps to be laboriously refilled and rekindled by night-fall each day. Battery operated minefield working lamps were eventually introduced, fitted with uni-directional shrouds and coloured filters. In turn, these were replaced by L-shaped plastic torches, whilst nowadays permanently illuminated Beta-light pointers provide very effective luminescent guides at night. Naturally, to prepare the fences and provide the lavish markings took time, manpower and resources that became less acceptable to allocate as the size of modern forces decreased and the need for speed increased. Rapid, lightweight breach marking was needed to keep pace with high tempo operations at minimum cost in manpower. Belgian and French forces share one such equipment, called the minefield lane marking set. It consists of a variety of signs, thin metal poles and yellow tape contained in 2 canvas bags. The US have produced an improvement on this in the M133 Hand Emplaced Minefield Marking Set (HEMMS). With the light posts and accessories, 4 men can mark up to 1000 metres in an hour. Even this excellent progress is improved upon by the Hunting

Lightweight Marking System, comprising plastic posts mounted on steel pins and connected by reflecting, yellow tape. The pins can be used on any earth surface and are tough enough to be hammered into tarmac. The kits are packaged into field satchels, each man-portable, and containing sufficient items to mark out 250 metres of minefield fence. With these kits, 2 men are able to erect fencing at rates in excess of 1000 metres per hour. At last, the passage of assault troops through a breach will not be delayed by the need to make the safe lane in the traditional and cumbersome fashion.

These official sets of equipment are designed to meet various national, international and alliance standards, specified in the past to ensure the safety of civilians and friendly forces and to warn an enemy of the danger presented by mines. Inevitably, stocks of marking stores are soon consumed in war and in some theatres their use is often inappropriate. When this is the case, improvisation comes to the fore. At the Second Battle of El Alamein, British engineers had to breach through many miles of German minefields. Lack of manpower and the need to pass troops through the gaps quickly, meant that standard marking

MARKING OF MINED TERRAIN

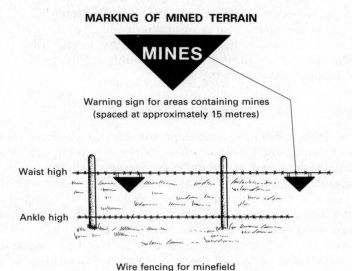

MINES

Warning sign for areas containing mines
(spaced at approximately 15 metres)

Waist high

Ankle high

Wire fencing for minefield

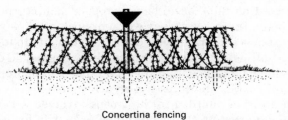

Concertina fencing

FIG. 7.1. *Marking of mined terrain. This is the ideal, when time and resources allow.*

procedures could not be completely followed. The method used to mark the centre line of many cleared routes was to stain the desert sand with waste oil. During the advance from Normandy, white tape was frequently laid to indicate the limits of mine free areas until rear echelon engineers could arrive to mark the breach properly. At times, make-shift signs were the only indication that mines were present and that a safe way forward had been found. Rough timber or scrap metal would be used as sign boards, having expressions such as "Road Not Checked" or Road Edge Mined", chalked or painted on by engineer reconnaissance parties amongst the advance elements of the leading formations. Each succeeding group of combat engineers would improve the standard of clearance and quality of marking to maintain the level of safety for the ever increasing volume of wheeled and unarmoured vehicles that were passing through. In different terrain, alternative marking methods were called for. British troops in Dhofar's rocky landscape used white paint for example, to identify safe routes cleared of AP mines, trip-wires and booby traps. A jungle environment presents particularly difficult problems for mine and booby trap detection, breaching and marking. Often local materials will be employed to warn of the presence of danger or to show a safe lane. It is very useful, particularly when operating against irregular forces in jungle, to become familiar with the enemy's system of hazard marking. The Viet Cong would angle a piece of broken bamboo at 45° and point it in the direction of a mine, to warn their own people of the danger. Elsewhere, a blazed tree, a broken branch or a stick poked through a leaf could all indicate the presence of mines to the knowing eye.

Mechanical Means

Despite the considerable improvements in the fencing of minefields and marking of breaches by hand, under some conditions these manual methods remain too slow for commanders and too dangerous for those taking part. An assault breaching operation, under fire from the defending force and with the risk of air and armed helicopter attack in addition, should not be attempted by men without the protection and mobility of AFVs if at all possible. A mechanical and speedy means of marking a breach is obviously needed. This was recognized many years ago and British armoured forces experimented with at least two systems prior to the invasion of Normandy. Both devices were planned to be fitted on to the rear of tanks pushing mine ploughs or rollers, thus, as a path was breached it would automatically be marked. One proposal envisaged a large hopper dispensing white chalk to mark the centre of the cleared route. The other system consisted of tall lamps, weighted at their base, being dropped behind the counter-measure vehicle. Surprisingly, these good ideas were dropped after World War II and the British Army has had to resurrect the requirement of late in its specification for a Vehicle Emplaced Minefield Marking Equipment. The battle experienced Israeli armoured forces have no such gap in their equipment inventory. The Clear Lane Marking System (CLAMS) indicates the breach centre line by day or night, with the maximum protection afforded to the troops involved. CLAMS is an entirely self-contained, add-on system that is designed primarily for fixing to the rear of MBT, but can be carried by most other military vehicles. It consists of a metal dispenser box, which can be operated automatically from a pre-settable control box within the AFV or manually by the crew. In automatic mode, the markers can be dispensed at intervals from 6 to 48 metres in 6-metre increments, to suit the terrain or light-levels at the time of the breach. If desired, two dispensers can be fitted at the edges of the tank rear to mark the limits of the breach, rather than the single dispenser, which normally marks the mid-point of the safe lane. Some 150 markers can be carried in each dispenser allowing quite a considerable length of route to be marked (900 metres to 7200 metres). The markers themselves come in 2 parts. The standard component is a circular metal base with a spring loaded red flag. A luminescent, 12 hour light-stick can be attached to the flag before dispensing for effective marking in poor visibility. CLAMS can also be used for rapid marking of emergency runways or operating strips and to indicate proven routes through difficult terrain. It is a simple system, currently in-service and available, setting a standard of effectiveness in an essential combat equipment, which all other mechanized forces should seek to emulate. Just as future breaching devices could be fitted to helicopters for rapid operations, so marking could also be carried out by rotary wing aircraft. This might be achieved through weighted markers or poles, or the dispersal of coloured plates, chalk or flourescent powder. Indeed this form of marking may be the only means that is sufficiently responsive and visible to cope with the difficulties anticipated in coping with airfield denial mines and the large safe areas that need to be identified for continued air operations. For this reason alone, further investigation into new marking systems is warranted.

A Counter-mine System

Present Deficiencies

Mine warfare is a constant battle between the mine and counter-measures to it. As a new mine or sensor is developed, a counter is immediately sought to negate it. If seen as successful, an improved mine is brought into service to defeat that counter-measure, and so the process is repeated. The basic SI mine was originally countered by explosive methods, such as the rocket-projected hose, or the mine roller. Long pulse fuzes were found to defeat explosive shock waves and DI fuzes were unaffected by rollers. The counter-mine plough was able to remove these new mines and consequently an anti-disturbance fuze became available to destroy the plough. At the same time, belly-attack mines were introduced. Track-width ploughs or rollers missed these and VEMASID type devices were needed to cope with their magnetic influence fuzes. Although these counter-measures did come into service, they were normally few in number and reserved for employment with the advanced elements of mobile forces. When SM and RDM made their appearance, it became apparent that all elements of a force were at risk from mines and that the detection and clearance of SM/RDM would be a massive challenge in both technical and quantitative terms. To this date no nation has a solution and it is known that this gap in counter-measure capability is of paramount concern to the most senior levels of the Warsaw Pact ground forces. Once it is confirmed that the Warsaw Pact has an acknowledged ability to deliver mines remotely, NATO nations will, no doubt, view the problem of clearing RDM with equal concern. Another group of mines that present a unique, and presently unresolved, counter-measure problem is ORM. With modern warheads and intelligent, tracking sensors such mines pose an underestimated threat to AFVs. The principal difficulty is locating these easily-concealed and passive devices, that are not susceptible to the existing range of counter-measures optimized to deal with track or belly attack mines. An additional predicament over detection arises in attempting to locate plastic or other non-metallic mines. As these are an increasing majority amongst the more straightforward, pressure-operated AP and AT mines it is essential to develop a monitor capable of detecting them reliably and accurately.

Principal Options

It is clear from the previous sections of this chapter that no one counter-measure can provide the panacea for all types of mine likely to be encountered. A selection of counter-mine procedures and equipment is required to permit the most appropriate measure to be adopted relative to the specific threat at that time and in that place. If there is a marked deficiency in any particular capability it is inevitable that a potential enemy will attempt to exploit that weakness by enhancing its stocks of the relevant munition. A complementary family of counter-measures is called for, containing the best from each type of counter-mine equipment. Of the mechanical systems, the most effective at present appears to be the track-width plough. It is faster in operation than both rollers and flails, having greater success against more types of mine than rollers and being less cumbersome than the flail. Although the flail does have a potential, full width, clearance capability its consistency against buried mines is questionable. Overall, the mine plough must be the recommended mechanical counter-measure, particularly as the MBT to which they are fitted remains free to manoeuvre and defend itself with its armament. Equally, SLUFAE is the outstanding means of explosive mine clearance. It has a greater stand-off than all other effective systems, providing it with exceptional flexibility and survivability. The length and width of breach are also more than can be achieved by any other explosive means. To deal with buried magnetic influence fuzed mines and similarly fuzed SM or RDM, the VEMASID principle is the preferred option. However, some RDM and many SM will have pressure fuzes and an alternative means of clearing these is necessary. A full width plough or dozer blade is likely to be the most expedient solution to this requirement. This selection of equipments is most appropriate for the breaching activities to be undertaken by mechanized, highly mobile forces. Few national forces have this need alone and most require the basic ability to detect and breach by hand. To do this satisfactorily a sensitive detector is essential, capable of locating metallic and non-metallic mines.

The Systems Approach

Whilst many armies have various items of counter-mine equipment it is probable that only a handful, if any, have an integrated mine counter-measure system that

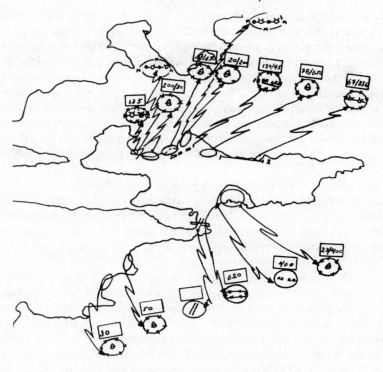

MALVINAS, 18 de Abril de 1982

FIG. 7.2. *Part of the inadequate minefield records employed by the Argentinians on the Falkland Islands.*

encompasses all the necessary aspects of dealing promptly and assuredly with mine obstacles. The total system would incorporate reconnaissance, communications, detection, breaching, marking and a reporting capacity to disseminate information on the safe routes. Central to the system is the command and control factor, which will be addressed within the complete context of mine warfare in the next chapter. For the moment, an example of a counter-mine system will be offered to illustrate the essential components and how they combine to result in a successful operation. The example is based upon an armoured division operating on rural terrain in an advance to contact. There is a potential threat from chemical or tactical nuclear weapons and the divisional commander will be seeking to advance at the best possible speed, whilst ensuring his force is never sufficiently concentrated to provide an attractive target for an enemy counter-stroke or nuclear attack. One concern will be obstacles. If at all possible, these will be by-passed or breached as rapidly as can be, to prevent the division from grinding to a halt or squashing upon itself against the obstruction.

The division is well equipped. Each of the armoured brigades in the force is mounted in MBT and IFV. Within each tank platoon, one MBT is fitted with track-width ploughs. The engineer unit in support of the division is also mechanized.

Combat engineers travel in APCs, whilst a temporarily attached assault engineer sub-unit holds FAE launchers and specialist engineer breaching vehicles, mounting full width mine ploughs forward, and marker dispensers on the rear. The divisional reconnaissance unit, ahead of the leading brigade, operates from light tanks working in pairs. It is one of these vehicles which reports the first contact of the battle.

In an over-watch position, it has observed its partner AFV erupt in flames as it made a high-speed dash across some open fields. The power of the explosion threw the vehicle on to its side and it can be reasonably assumed that a mine was the cause. Closer observation by the recce crew, confirmed by adjacent pairs of recce tanks, reveals that enemy mine signs can be seen across the front of the leading brigade's axis. As some of the recce force begin to move off to the sides in an attempt to find a way around the minefield, the recce leader informs the forward brigade commander of the obstacle. A tank unit is immediately ordered forward to make a hasty crossing. With 2 companies of tanks hull down, ready to provide covering fire, the third advances in platoon columns on to the mined area — plough tanks leading. As they move well into the minefield, artillery, but not other, fire is directed on to the MBT. Well protected by their thick armour, the shell fire has little effect on the success of the rapid breach. Followed by the second and third companies in the same tracks, the unit fans out once on the enemy side of the minefield, its commanding officer reporting the co-ordinates of the cleared lanes to his brigade headquarters and expressing his opinion that it was a minimal minefield, designed to impose limited delay and encourage fear of mines in the advancing troops. As the recce groups once more resume the lead, probing forward, the front brigade will continue its advance using the initial breaches opened up by its own plough tanks. Other recce troops may have found routes around the minefield to allow follow-up elements to by-pass the obstacle. In any event, some of the divisional combat engineers would be despatched to the initial breach areas, with the task of marking the safe lanes and ensuring that all mines had been cleared from the routes.

As the division moves deeper into the battle zone, more and more incidents will arise. Demolished bridges will need replacing, air attack will take its toll, tank ambushes will reduce the strength of the recce force and embroil the units of the forward brigade in many, varied engagements. All the time, brigade and unit commanders and divisional staff will be aware of the general's insistence to accept no delay, to maintain the momentum of the formation and seek a high tempo in all operational activities. For he will be intent on dispensing with the minor and irritating attempts to dissipate his division's fighting strength and reduce its rate of advance, in order to close on to the enemy's main position and break through into the less protected areas beyond.

At last, his intelligence staff advise him that every indicator points to the fact that the leading brigade is being engaged by enemy main forces. Reports show that recce elements are finding it impossible to proceed further due to violent and persistent direct fire against them. A large minefield has been met and an attempt by a tank unit at a hasty breach was met initially by ATGW, then MBT main armament fire. The operation was called off when at least two of the plough-tanks were destroyed, possibly by belly-attack mines. Using a procedure well practised in peace, a deliberate breaching operation is ordered using a reserve brigade and the assault engineer sub-unit. As the brigade begins its move forward, a fearful air attack leaves the way forward blocked by air delivered, area denial mines. Those tank units with mine ploughs are able to move forward slowly, trying not to allow mines to lie between the tracks and attack hull bellies, until the full width engineer ploughs gain the point position and clear safe routes forward for the assault brigade. Eventually, the formation is deployed for the major attack across the enemy's tactical minefield. Under cover of a heavy artillery concentration on to identified enemy positions, the FAE rockets are fired in a breach pattern on to the minefield, the boundaries of which had been reported by the original recce troops. Not trusting that the FAE have destroyed all buried, belly attack mines in the field, the first vehicles on to the selected lines of the breach are the full width engineer ploughs that mark the safe routes as they clear them. Their efforts are supported by covering smoke from mortars, and the guns and ATGW of the well positioned leading brigade. Once clear of the rear of the minefield, the engineer plough crews can call forward the assault brigade, which finds its way through the breach, following the luminous lane markers despite the smoke, flames and dust of battle.

This brief and simplified explanation of a possible counter-measure system highlights the fact that counter-mine warfare is not solely an engineer responsibility. Much of the expertise and equipment will reside within combat engineer and assault pioneer units, but the underlying requirement for a rapid response demands that some counter-mine capability is held internally within tank and infantry units. It is also incumbent upon reconnaissance forces to be able to recognize enemy minefields and hazard signs, in order to alert formation staffs early of the breaching tasks that may have to be faced. The entire, all arms system for breaching must also be fully exercised in peace to weld the diverse units together, to practise the staff procedures and to prove the communications links. Normally, the opportunities for field training above unit level in combined arms groups are rare and commanders often wish to practise their troops in more mobile operations than minefield breaching. However, deliberate breaching is a complex activity that should not be undertaken lightly, without preparation or rehearsal. The peacetime tendency to ignore minefields on exercises, or reduce their tactical significance, will be disastrously misleading in war. A study of British experience in World War II has shown that in more than twenty instances, tank regiments were delayed in excess of 15 hours by minefield obstacles. Bulling through the mines is no answer, and *ad hoc* reactions at the last moment will prove little better. The constitution of a counter-measure system, which has been competently devised and energetically exercised, will be a major factor in successful counter-mine operations by highly mobile, armoured forces. The present balance of mine versus counter-measure is weighed in favour of the mine. The variety and lethality of modern mines makes it exceptionally difficult to counter them, and the situation will deteriorate as the more complex, third generation devices enter service. Attention to counter-measures has not kept pace with the improvements in mines, consequently more research is needed into counter-mine options. To have any chance of dealing effectively with the threat of mines on the battlefield, those counter-measures which do exist must be ordered sensibly into a robust and flexible system. Without this logical mustering of resources and expertise, the limited counter-measure facilities that do exist in a military force will be squandered on local, perhaps minor, tasks. They will be unavailable at the critical moment for a priority operation that might otherwise win the battle. And this is precisely the situation a defender would like to see opponents placed in by his minefield preparations: lacking mobility, denuded of resources and ripe for defeat.

8

Command and Control

MINE warfare is a complex undertaking. Mine and counter-mine operations involve decision making by tactical and engineer commanders at many levels, followed by a mass of detailed liaison and co-ordination between headquarters staffs and units. So far this has been a manpower intensive effort, inevitably slow and time-consuming. Yet modern mines and counter-measures are being introduced that reduce laying and breaching times drastically. To maximize upon the benefits available from these equipments it is necessary to streamline combat engineer command and control procedures. This chapter examines current practice and existing communications technology with a view to recommending an improved system for the battlefield management of mine warfare.

Military Organization

The arms and services in a military force are traditionally separated into three groups. The infantry and armoured units form the combat arms, who are closely aided by the supporting arms, namely the artillery, combat engineers, army aviation and signals units. The logistic services, such as transport, ordnance and maintenance, provide the material support without which an army in the field could not exist. Holding this diverse mix of units together are the formation commanders and staff officers, operating out of static or mobile headquarters and communicating over links provided by specialist signals units. The units of armour and infantry are the basis of the battle groups, which respond to the manoeuvre orders from brigade or divisional headquarters. Each country will have its own favoured organization for the tactical formations within its armed forces, resulting from its present requirements and past experiences. A parachute brigade, for example, could consist of two or three airborne battalions, whilst an armoured brigade may contain two tank battalions plus a mechanized infantry unit. Divisions might comprise two, three or more brigades and an army corps would be formed from several divisions. At every formation level there are combat support and logistic units to provide specialist services. Typically, a brigade's slice might include an artillery battalion, a combat engineer company, an ordnance supply unit and a maintenance workshop. At divisional levels, heavier gun support will be found, along with specialist engineer units, army helicopters, transport units, air defence assets and military hospitals. More exclusive and expensive resources are reserved for deployment by corps headquarters, they could include electronic warfare (EW) battalions, surface to surface missile units, amphibious bridging equipments and attack helicopter squadrons. The formations are organized into a hierarchical pyramid: a corps headquarters controlling divisions, which command brigades, which in turn deploy the units. The principal staff branches in these headquarters are those of operations and intelligence. Information is assessed by the intelligence staff and passed to the formation commander to aid him in his decision making. Once he has a plan he will pass the outline to his operations staff, who put it into effect with the assistance of the logistics staff. The plan a commander decides upon is rarely of his individual making, for he relies heavily upon the specialist advice received from the appropriate arm or service commander. These officers might be permanent members of the headquarters, with their own staff section, or could be unit commanders available to provide the formation commander with their specific expertise. Thus, there are parallel chains of command within a field formation. There is the central strand, emanating from the authority of the tactical commander and passing through the operations cells of the subordinate headquarters. The alternative links are provided by arm and service staffs at each comparable level of headquarters, who issue technical instructions to the lower staffs and units of their own discipline.

An example will help to clarify how this complex matrix of command and control operates in practice. Imagine a corps deployed on defensive operations, with an armoured division forming its reserve force. An enemy night assault has had limited success, several tank battalions having broken through to occupy a salient within the defence zone. EW intercept of enemy signals traffic suggests that a second assault wave is being reorganized to attack through this bridge-head and exploit the initial gains. Satellite reconnaissance confirms that enemy reserves are being diverted towards the salient. This information is assessed by corps intelligence staffs, who advise the commander of likely enemy intentions. From the area of the salient, conversations between commanders at the various levels plus reports sent upwards on the operations net, reveal that local counter-attacks are failing to dislodge the enemy armour and the dangerous incursion into the depth of the defensive position remains a reality. In order to maintain the integrity of his defended area, the corps commander decides to employ his reserve division in a counter-move. After a rapid assessment of the situation with his chief of staff, senior logistics staff officer and artillery, engineer and air advisers, a plan is formulated and he directs the commander of his reserve division to mount an operation. This will involve a counter-penetration task close to the original FEBA, in order to deny the bridge-head any reinforcements, whilst the remainder of the division counter-attack those enemy positions within the salient. At corps level an outline operation instruction must be prepared and issued, not only to the reserve division conducting the primary operation, but to many other addresses. The army group headquarters above corps level will need to know that a major counter-move is being planned, as will those divisions below in the area of the bridge-head. Equally, all the support arms, services and air force agencies, who may be required to assist in the operation, have to be alerted. Many of these agencies will have been consulted by the corps commander or his senior staff in formulating the plan, and they will have been co-ordinating their

PLATE 7.1. *The infantryman of the future, equipped with mine-resistant boots and body armour.*

PLATE 7.2. *A mine-resistant troop carrier in service with the Defence Forces of South Africa.*

PLATE 7.3. *Body armour provided for an EOD specialist, searching an incident area with a SWEEP probe.*

PLATE 7.4. *Courage, skill and concentration. No Sapper could afford to make a slip in disarming a German grenade mine.*

PLATE 7.5. *Training in mine breaching drills under realistic tactical conditions in NBC protective clothing, with gloves and respirators close to hand.*

PLATE 7.6. *Dogs have a long history in the task of mine detection. Here they are used to clear a railway line in World War II.*

PLATE 7.7. *Full width mine rollers, too heavy to be a realistic proposition in war.*

PLATE 7.8. *Mine clearance rollers fitted to an MBT. Note the separate rollers fitted in parallel to simplify replacement after mine damage.*

PLATE 7.9. *ROBAT — an advanced minefield breaching concept from the United States.*

PLATE 7.10. *The Aardvark flail — a new treatment of a battle-proven concept.*

PLATE 7.11. *An early World War II version of the track width mine plough.*

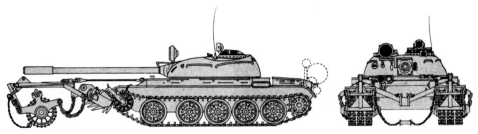

PLATE 7.12. *Soviet counter-measures: a T-54 equipped with PT-54 rollers (TOP) and a T-55 mounting the KMT-5 plough and roller combination.*

PLATE 7.13. *Track width mine ploughs fitted to an armoured vehicle of the Royal Engineers.*

PLATE 7.14. *A unique minefield breaching system: Giant Vipers in tandem towed by an AVRE equipped with track width mine ploughs.*

PLATE 7.15. *The counter obstacle vehicle fitted with full width mine ploughs.*

PLATE 7.16. *A major counter-measure problem — the clearance of remotely delivered mines.*

PLATE 7.17. *A mine clearance ladder ready for extension by a simple rocket device.*

PLATE 7.18. *The moment of detonation of a Giant Viper.*

PLATE 7.19. *The tell-tale smoke plume from a Giant Viper detonation.*

PLATE 7.20. *Rapid marking of minefields or gaps with a lightweight marking system.*

PLATE 8.1. *A hand-held digital communications terminal offers rapid and accurate dissemination of mine warfare data.*

PLATE 8.2. *A tactical message entry device, with cryptographic and burst transmission facilities, matching easily to modern combat radios.*

PLATE 8.3. *Phoenix — the British Army's first RPV.*

PLATE 8.4. *A joint service Integrated Command System (ICS), featuring computerized data management and a graphics display facility. Miniaturized and hardened, this type of technology could form the basis of a tactical mine warfare command and control system.*

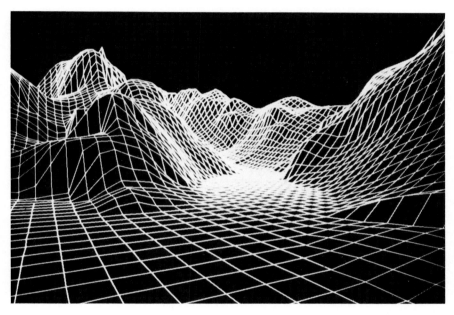

PLATE 8.5. *Digital terrain modelling can play an important role in the selection of minefield locations.*

PLATE 8.6. *Lasermap — a battlefield map display system employing symbology overlay and background map projection.*

PLATE 9.1. *The MCV 80 is a recent addition to the growing number and variety of AFVs on the battlefield that aggravate the problems of mine design.*

PLATE 9.2. *Merkava. Despite the added protection such a design offers against frontal attack, this is the only front-engined MBT in service.*

PLATE 9.3. *The Apache attack helicopter. A formidable weapon system, typical of the growing helicopter threat to ground forces, that may be countered by an anti-helicopter mine.*

PLATE 9.4. *DROPS — a new concept for rapid handling of logistic loads such as mines or ammunition.*

specialist requirements concurrently with the efforts of the operations staff. For example, the engineer commander will have left the corps commander's command post knowing that part of the reserve division will be employed in counter-penetration. Anticipating the likely request from that force for additional mines, mine layers and entrenching equipment he will have returned to the engineer staff vehicle to confirm the availability of such items. His staff would begin the release or reallocation process for men and material, advising the corps operations staff of the quantities and types of stores and titles of units assigned to the counter-move, to allow this information to be included in their instruction. Engineer staffs and units at lower levels would begin to co-ordinate the collection and movement of stores and equipment, and arrange the concentration of sapper units in suitable hide locations.

Whilst all the specialist staffs are making similar assumptions and taking anticipatory action, the divisional commander and his principal advisers will be engaged in reconnaissance and planning for the operation. Eventually, based upon the corps instruction and the divisional commander's directive, the operations staff at divisional level will prepare and issue a detailed operation order that finalizes timings, organizations, objectives and the allocation of resources. When this is received, there should be few surprises contained within it. For each of the specialist staff sections and units will be aware of their expected part in the battle, as a result of the previous notification down technical command channels. The manoeuvre units will also be preparing for their coming role in the fighting. They receive information directly from brigade commanders or operations staffs, being the priority out-stations on command or operations nets. This concurrent activity at each level of a force, up and down parallel command and communications channels, is known as battle procedure. It is a major training objective to inculcate this practice of rapid and multidirectional co-ordination and information dissemination. Its purpose is to reduce to an absolute minimum the time that must be spent in mounting an operation. In many cases, time can be a commander's greatest enemy and he will strive to dominate the time factor in all his calculations. Time, too, can be the most limited of resources and a sense of urgency is vital in any military force. This does not imply that hasty, uncoordinated actions are required in an attempt to beat the clock, but rather officers and soldiers must be so well-trained in their duties and exercised alongside their colleagues, that competence and mutual understanding exist to such an extent as to allow simultaneous, rapid activity to take place within the broadest of guidelines from commanders and senior staff officers. This standard of effective battle procedure can only be achieved when an elaborate matrix of command and communications channels is available within a force. A formation commander must have easy access to the advice he needs from supporting arms and service commanders. Since modern forces are complex and varied, designated commanders are required to control the technical elements and it is they who are best placed to inform the tactical commander about the capabilities, limitations, availability and use of specialist troops. In turn, these functional commanders act as the initial conduit for the intentions of the tactical commander. Using specific-to-arm channels, they initiate the procedures, which lead to the infantry and armoured units receiving the combat support that is required. This flexible

and responsive command structure is essential to a successful military organization and is heavily dependent upon reliable communications.

Communications

EW is a significant, if secretive, component of modern combat. It covers a host of
applications from the deception of enemy weapon systems, through the suppres-
sion of air defence radars, to the area of communications. In this latter field it can
vary in use to include the intercept of transmissions to obtain information, the
cross-referencing of transmitting stations by separate direction-finding facilities
to accurately locate the transmitter through triangulation prior to its subsequent
physical destruction, or the jamming of signals considered to be important to the
enemy at a specific period in time. Military communications must operate in this
extremely hostile environment and survive the electronic and physical attacks
made upon them. The multiplicity of command channels referred to above aids in
defending the survivability of the communications system, as messages can be
passed on alternative routes if a specific net is rendered inoperative. However,
this is a temporary and undesirable solution as channels become congested and
concurrent activity is inhibited. Communications systems are required, which are
intrinsically resistant to EW. One method of avoiding the problem is to use
despatch riders, another is to employ liaison officers, and if time permits the
laying of land-line is yet another. Motor-cycle despatch riders are an essential aid
to communications under conditions of radio and electronic silence. They are
reasonably fast, with a good cross-country capability and afford excellent carrying
capacity. But they are vulnerable. The riders quickly become tired, they have a
tendency to get lost and are unprotected, with only mobility as a means of defence.
Liaison officers mounted in small, preferably armoured, vehicles offer a more
flexible option. Montgomery used personal liaison officers to good effect, by
sending them out to bring back current information which he required. In this
way, undiluted facts were relayed to him personally at best speed. Land-line or
field cable is time consuming to lay and vulnerable to traffic, sabotage and
artillery fire. But if time permits it is worth laying and protecting a land-line
circuit within headquarters or defensive positions, as a reliable, non-radiating
means of internal communication. Despite the availability of the alternatives and
the dangers of EW, the most common form of military communication is based
upon the radio bands of the electromagnetic spectrum. Speed, convenience and
ever-improving electronic technology are the factors which drive the military
towards increasing dependence upon a wide range of radio based systems.

Combat Net Radio (CNR) is the most common form of communications at the
unit and lower formation levels. CNR relies upon VHF, and to a lesser extent HF,
transmissions. Although VHF offers better quality signals than HF, it does have a
shorter propagation range than HF. Nevertheless, VHF is adequate for most unit
requirements and forms the basis of the majority of military equipments. CNR
tends to be used in a cellular manner. For example, each company in a battalion
will have a unique internal frequency, which will change each day. Radios within
that company could be on a generous scale, allowing an issue to every AFV and
the distribution of dismountable, manpack versions down to every officer and

section. Every element of that company can then communicate on its unique frequency without interference from other parts of the battalion. To co-ordinate the actions of the companies and support elements, a battalion command net will be set-up on a separate frequency. This process is repeated at brigade level, where its command net will have a considerable number of outstations including the commanders and headquarters of the tank, infantry, artillery, engineer and aviation units. In addition to being on a brigade net, the combat support and logistic units will have to man at least two additional nets. One will be the unit's own command net to control its sub-units and attachments. In the case of an engineer battalion this net will reach down to the combat engineer companies, to the support echelon and engineer workshop, and encompass assault engineer or bridging sub-units that may be temporarily attached for a specific operation. The other net to be manned is the specialist net of the next most senior arm or service commander. Consequently, the engineer unit will also be an outstation on the divisional commander engineers' radio net. This purely engineer net provides the channel for disseminating special-to-arm instructions and information. The engineer unit can call for stores, mines, demolitions or earthmoving equipment on this sapper channel, liaise with other engineer units or receive warning orders as higher formation staffs receive an indication of likely future tasks. The loop is completed by the divisional engineer staff being on the divisional command net alongside the brigades. In this way, an assessment of the operational situation or a review of the commander's intentions originating in the divisional operations cell could reach an engineer unit via the divisional net to a brigade headquarters, where it would be retransmitted on the brigade net, or via the commander engineers net from the divisional engineer staff branch. This network of parallel links across formations and down through them offers a measure of flexibility of routing and a consequent resistance to EW. But additional defences are necessary to guarantee a capability of continuous operation under EW conditions. Various techniques are available to achieve this. A widely used method of denying information on radio links is to use cryptographic equipment. In the past, cryptography has been restricted to vehicle installations due to the size of the equipment required. This is no longer the case and short range, hand-held radios can now be fitted with add-on crypto modules to provide a secure communications link. The Racal-Comsec MA 4225 encryption set is typical of this new generation of equipment. Alternative counter-measures include frequency hopping, as used in Plessey System 4000, in-band spread spectrum techniques, burst transmissions, and the use of interference cancellation, through steerable null antenna processing. The simplicity of operation of VHF sets nowadays, typified by the UK Clansman series, and their general availability have given rise to a saturation of the VHF band of the spectrum by the proliferation of sets and users. To find more communications space and obtain additional range, it is possible to move into the HF band.

Traditionally, HF has been avoided as more skilled operators have been needed to ensure reliable communications in the noisy background conditions, and transmission success is dependent upon the time of day and the frequency selected. To a great extent these objections are now overcome by the development of devices such as the Rockwell-Collins Selscan. This equipment uses microprocessor technology to provide automatic connectivity, through a search and store technique, which locates the best channel to communicate over. Vast ranges, thousands of kilometres in fact, can be achieved with HF, or alternatively it can be used over tactically acceptable ranges. At these shorter ranges, HF has most often been employed as a dormant reserve to VHF command nets at formation headquarters levels. With the miniaturization of circuits and power supplies it has become possible to manpack HF sets, such that they play a full part in tactical combat communications. However, CNR provides an all-informed facility, ideal for tactical units, but less suitable for the one-to-one conversations that can be most valuable to formation commanders and their staffs. Equally, staff branches need the ability to pass large amounts of data, rapidly, securely and accurately. To do this over CNR would deny the nets to other users, whilst errors and repetitions would be inevitable. To overcome these disadvantages, and offer extended facilities to formation commanders or staffs, trunk communication systems have been developed.

A trunk network has to be reliable, with high capacity, and the ability to handle voice, telegraph, data and facsimile traffic. The radio relay systems, which offer these capabilities, are usually operating in the SHF and UHF bands. These systems are deployed in one of two modes. Early trunk networks were based upon the chain-of-command principle, in which the radio relay stations or nodes are located close to the headquarters they support. The British Bruin system is configured in this manner. To meet more demanding operational requirements and prevent the mobility of a force being limited by its associated signal network, the area system has come to the fore. In this network, the nodes are distributed carefully throughout the area of operations, independent of any affiliated headquarters. This lattice is virtually invulnerable to disruption as there are so many possible routes for messages around the grid, unlike the limited number of connections available from a hierarchical chain-of-command system. The new Ptarmigan area trunk network being introduced into 1st British Corps is an ideal example of the type of high-technology, survivable system that can be fielded nowadays. It is the form of network which the US forces are seeking to meet their Tri-Tac programme requirement. This is the tactical, high volume, switching, communications system they wish to optimize for the control of forces operating under the Airland Battle 2000 concept. Other nations have the need for trunk communications and several have been developed: the French Rita, Norwegian Delta Mobile and Dutch Zodiac are just some of those available. The Ptarmigan system offers a radio telephone facility to certain users, such as unit and formation commanders, which provides instant access to the main trunk network. Even those with CNR sets can gain entry to the system through an interface equipment, and the trunk network has additional interface modules that permit connection to HF troposcatter or satellite links, to the civil telephone system, to air force bases and to higher or adjacent formations. Above all, Ptarmigan provides a secure, computer-controlled, common carrier that is especially suited to the needs of modern mobile forces and to the demands of headquarters for high integrity, digital data communications. For those nations with less complex requirements, or a need for a more lightweight system, there is the Marconi Claymore digital radio relay system. Based upon mobile trunk radio terminals and microprocessor controlled switching equipment, all of which can be mounted in landrover size vehicles, Claymore offers a unique communications capability to marine, airportable or similar rapid deployment forces.

Information

Improved communications have not only permitted commanders to pass orders more quickly and manoeuvre their forces more promptly, but have also allowed lower echelons to provide up-to-date information on an unprecedented scale. Another phenomenon has added to this virtual explosion of tactical information. This is the increase in sensor systems that current technology can make available. Soldiers can now see at night with image intensifiers or thermal imagery devices; they can observe the battlefield through fog, rain and snow with radar; and remote sensor systems such as Racal's Classic or Marconi's Hermes equipments need no operator to be within 30 kilometres of them, yet can report the movement of men and vehicles automatically to a distant monitor. Even more information will be fed into headquarters as remotely piloted vehicles (RPV), and developments such as Phoenix and Castor, enter service. The RPV has been proven in combat by the Israeli forces during their occupation of Southern Lebanon in 1982. Their Scout and Mastiff RPVs, carrying remotely-controlled TV cameras, provided the invading troops with a real-time reconnaissance and battlefield intelligence gathering capability. Phoenix is an RPV based surveillance and target acquisition system required by the British Army, likely to employ a thermal imaging detector. The intention is that Phoenix will be cued on to areas of interest by the Corps Airborne Stand-Off Radar (CASTOR), an airborne, medium-altitude, multi-role radar solution to the demand for a Corps level, area surveillance capability out to medium ranges. This complementary mix of new sensor systems will be used principally to locate targets for long range artillery and close support aircraft. However, RPVs equipped with alternative sensor pods, containing high resolution TV cameras or forward looking infrared (FLIR) detectors, could easily act in the minefield detection role, amongst other reconnaissance functions.

Even before this increased volume of information entered headquarters, it was difficult for staffs to handle the amount of detail they received verbally, or in reports, or over the radios and telephones in their cells. An accurate picture of the battle situation is always difficult to obtain for a variety of reasons. Information becomes distorted as it passes through the various levels of a command hierarchy, as each level applies its own interpretation to the data arriving from below, before passing it on higher. Information quickly becomes dated, particularly when it concerns very mobile forces, and this is especially true for location reports. Few headquarters can testify to the exact location of all of their units, except under very static conditions. And information also has a tendency to get lost, either as a result of disrupted communications, or more likely because of an inadequate storage facility. It is also true that, on occasions, headquarters have failed to disseminate information downwards, that was vital to the battle but never made available to combat troops in need of it. These failings of the traditional staff system were recognized as early as the end of World War II, when the large, mechanized formations of the Allied invasion forces outstripped the communications, staff and logistic support that was available. The impossibility of controlling forces engaged in highly mobile operations by manual staff methods was similarly confirmed during the Yom Kippur War, when higher commands on both sides were unaware for long periods that whole battalions, even brigades, had suffered destruction. Evidently, a major revision of staff procedures and techniques was called for to cope with the processing, assessment and dissemination of the wide range and increasing amounts of information entering headquarters at an accelerating rate. If technology had aggravated the information handling problem, it did at least provide a solution in the advent of automatic data processing (ADP).

Battlefield computers are becoming ever more evident amongst military forces across the world, as their range of applications grows and they become more acceptable to users, initially sceptical over their ruggedness and reliability. Small devices proliferate to aid the individual soldier in his basic duties, one of the most common being the hand-held mortar fire control computer, closely followed by tactical digital message terminals, which enable checked reports to be despatched over CNR in burst transmission form. At headquarters automated command and control systems are gradually being introduced to provide message handling, graphic map displays and tabular based information entry, update and retrieval facilities. Wavell is the system being adopted by 1st British Corps, capable of handling and manipulating intelligence, operations, logistic, artillery and engineer data in a series of fixed formats, it eases the tedious and mundane workload previously placed on staff officers. The Bundeswehr Heros ADP system and the US Army Sigma manoeuvre control system will provide comparable opportunities for their headquarters staff to be released from routine tasks and play a more active, evaluative role in the control of the battle. Whilst these systems tend to cater for the central operations and intelligence staffs, little has been done to automate the staff work of other branches except for the artillery. The original attempts at automating artillery control procedures, exemplified by the US Army Tacfire and French Atila projects, have been superseded by smaller, rugged and more mobile developments such as Philips' Linda and the British Army's Battlefield Artillery Target Engagement System (BATES). The latter links forward observers, gun and missile positions, unit command posts, and artillery staff cells, providing them with ADP for targeting, ballistic and meteorological calculations, together with the control of artillery movements and logistic support. Of special interest amongst the display devices provided for BATES is the plasma panel VDU terminal, which has a graphics capability. However, this equipment is presently too large to be of practical use to the most forward elements of the artillery chain. Consequently, a self-contained, man-portable, digital map display module is being sought for FOOs, that is capable of being updated directly by the Phoenix RPV. Ferranti Defence Systems have demonstrated a portable map display, which can accept superimposed images derived from either radar or thermal imagery sensors to meet this requirement and Litton Data Systems offer a family of lightweight processors, some with a full screen, graphic display and all with a communications capability, that are in current service with US forces.

Command, Control, Communications and Intelligence (C^3I) is a recent entry into the world of military terminology, yet one that is widely known and overwhelmingly important. In simple terms it covers the exercise of passing information from the lowest front-line echelons to the highest commander, and the despatch of his resulting instructions back down to the fighting soldier. Since the beginning of this chapter, the complexity and frustrations of achieving a successful measure of C^3I have been outlined and the contribution that modern technology is playing to overcome the inherent difficulties has been illustrated. C^3I systems facilitate the collection, classification, processing, storage, display and distribution of information, but they do not make decisions or choose between alternative options. These tasks continue to face a commander and his staff. Nevertheless, such responsibilities are simplified by the availability of accurate and reliable data on which more informed decisions can be made, more rapidly. As these automated systems become available, supported by high capacity trunk communications and intelligent peripherals, their employment will expand into areas not originally envisaged. One role for C^3I that has so far been neglected, but is evidently in need of systematic attention, is that of mine warfare command and control.

Mine Warfare Requirements

Planning

In a defensive situation, the plan for battle is conceived by the tactical commander after an appreciation of all those factors likely to influence his decision. He will be advised throughout this process by the specialist commanders available to him, one of whom will undoubtedly be the engineer commander. Part of the engineer advice will concern the number of units, amount of equipment and quantity of mines that can be made available to support the defensive battle. These parameters can be combined to offer a variety of options to the tactical commander on what length, depth, density and number of minefields can be prepared in the time available, by the sappers to hand, with the resources at their disposal. If the defence is being planned under combat conditions, perhaps in great haste, then the engineer commander and his staff will have little time to undertake elaborate calculations and it may be that only one option can be presented for consideration in the time available. This is quite likely, as there are many different layouts for minefields, each of which will take a finite period to design. Using the mix of alternative mines available with a choice of fuzes, in different sequences and numbers, at varying densities, a whole range of possibilities could be generated to provide the required stopping power against specific target arrays. In peacetime, tables can be prepared to show how mines and fuzes can be arranged to obtain a certain effect against standard, anticipated targets. These tables are valuable thereafter, when minefields have to be designed in a hurry, although they tend to be very complicated and caution needs to be observed when their accurate use is required. Despite the availability of such design tables, the multiplicity of potential options arising from time, terrain and resource parameters, plus the alternatives added by tactical choice, produce an unwieldy number of solutions that cannot be computed manually with ease, or readily displayed in digestible form. If defensive plans are being formulated in a more deliberate manner, then it may be possible to calculate and list the possible mix of minefields by type, number and size and display those options on a number of maps or overlays. However, it would be simple to devise a program, capable of being run on present military computers, to calculate the blend of minefields that could be prepared with the transport, mines, laying or delivery equipments and manpower allocated to the obstacle plan. This output could be presented in a variety of suitable ways, the most useful probably being that in graphic form. Computer generated map displays can be superimposed with the outlines of possible minefields in rapid succession until the preferred layout is agreed. Automating the design process will be even more valuable when time is short and almost instantaneous response is required. It is under these conditions that the manual calculation is most open to error and the limited choice of options is least acceptable. This requirement for some form of ADP assistance in registering mine warfare resources and planning their subsequent utilization cannot be underestimated. Quantities of mines are often measured in hundreds of thousands, weighing thousands of tons, that must be transported according to a complex movement plan. These arrrangements are prone to disruption from a variety of sources, such that the mines which actually arrive in a combat engineer unit could be quite different from those originally envisaged. Having agreed the desired obstacle plan with the tactical commander and his operations staff, the engineer commander may have to re-appraise the formation commander of revised options at, literally, the last moment. Attempting to collate incoming information on mines physically received by laying units, and comparing those holdings with the original outloading plan, will be difficult enough. But to hope to reconcile those holdings with the minefield layouts required by the battle plan will be virtually impossible using normal staff procedures. A computerized inventory control system, with the capacity to calculate minefield designs and dimensions, will simplify the problem of resource assessment and option presentation to such an extent that almost instantaneous reaction to a situation can be achieved. Flexibility and speed of response are basic objectives of a military force, the pursuit of which permeates almost every activity. It is perfectly proper that modern, available technology should be harnessed to provide these characteristics in the planning phase of mine warfare operations.

Terrain Analysis

Within the planning cycle, modern computers can play a new role in the difficult terrain evaluation process too. It is now possible to digitize the information held previously on maps, overlays or battle plans and store it as data. Vegetation, soil types, gradients and ground bearing pressure can be included on the data base too. This computerized cartography is an accepted discipline of military survey these days, such that software packages have been developed to meet the demands previously placed on topographical sections of the armed forces in support of military operations. Consequently, the vast amount of stored terrain data can be displayed and manipulated to the specific requirements of a tactical commander with great ease. The increasing availability of C^3I systems, with graphics capable terminals or map display panels, enables the commander to view computer generated images of the terrain in many novel ways. Initially, the ground could be presented in the orthodox, two-dimensional fashion that is revealed from any map. Information can then be removed or added as required. For example, the ground favourable to the passage of AFVs can be highlighted whilst that impassable to tracked vehicles is subdued. This clearly indicates to the tactical and engineer commanders what the most likely approach routes may be for enemy armoured forces. Weapon system characteristics can be programmed in, to allow preferred defensive locations to be determined from intervisibility calculations, that are automatically computed and displayed. Thus the best positions for siting weapons to cover potential enemy routes can be discovered. At that point it will be evident where obstacles should be placed: to deny access to areas not adequately protected by fire, to block the most feasible avenues of approach or to protect troop positions. In order to confirm aspects of the plan unfolding on the screen, the terrain model can be generated as a three-dimensional view from any direction and the commander can appreciate how the demolitions or minefields will appear to an advancing enemy or to his own forces. Normally, commanders would wish to carry out a ground reconnaissance to enable them to visualize the actual countryside that their troops will be operating over, and this terrain appreciation should be undertaken if at all possible. However, some situations will arise when this is impossible: when the enemy has total, local air superiority; if nuclear or chemical contamination is present; or more usually, the objective may be in enemy territory, perhaps a target for RDM, amphibious assault or a counter-stroke.

On these occasions, digital terrain information displays, updated by satellite, air or RPV reconnaissance, will be far superior to the use of standard maps for planning and briefing. As the data is stored in digital form it is also a much simpler matter than ever before to disseminate the plans and supporting information to those lower headquarters who need it. Once the senior commander has superimposed his plan on to the appropriate terrain display, to show boundaries, routes, locations and minefields, he can cause the same display to be switched to any other user on his C^{3}I network with a suitable terminal. Using conference call facilities on the same network, he can explain his concept of operations, pointing with an electronic marker, whilst all are watching the identical image. For those not on the C^{3}I system, or lacking graphics facilities, the plotters and printers allied to the network will produce hard copy. The computer graphics package outlined above is of far greater value to a tactical commander than purely as an obstacle planning aid, since terrain modelling can also assist in communication system planning, wargaming, or radar, air defence and artillery siting. However, its use in deciding the position of obstacles can be taken even beyond the proposals discussed so far. It is feasible to model a terrain's natural resistance to any form of vehicle and thus estimate how far an enemy might advance in a given time, without artificial hindrance. Time/distance contours can then be drawn, to show areas where an advance would be deepest. On those occasions when time is at a premium, such as the unexpected break-through by an enemy force, the availability of these time/distance overlays will save precious hours of reconnaissance and map appreciation in deciding the critical points to be blocked by SM, RDM or rapid demolitions. Of course, these defensive applications of terrain analysis are but one side of the coin. Terrain evaluation will be equally valuable in the advance, prior to an attack, ahead of a withdrawal or before a counter-move. Routes can be selected; choke points identified, to be seized by helicopter assault; and approaches to vulnerable flanks located, to be closed by RDM or troops. Digital terrain techniques are thus a valuable and practical tool, which should be adopted widely in support of both military and engineer operations. To ignore the potential of this particular aid, is to deny a force a uniquely responsive capability.

Reporting

Despite the great advances in sensor technology one of the most difficult tasks for an advancing soldier is to detect, locate and identify his enemy. The defender will have taken great trouble to conceal and camouflage his position from ground and air observation, to surprise an attacker at his time of choosing. Although those defended positions may have been detected by satellite, air reconnaissance, RPV or EW, there is no guarantee that the information will ever reach the assault echelon. Even should it do so, the information will not be sufficiently detailed to allow the soldiers manning weapons to engage targets. They must search along their axis of advance for any tell-tale sign of a potential target and probe with fire to generate a response. Well-trained troops will hold their fire, despite this provocation, until the attacker is in the selected killing ground, perhaps stranded on a minefield and in range of all defending weapons. This is a situation, in which no assault force wishes to find itself, hence the emphasis on reconnaissance. But the surveillance and reconnaissance effort is not simply directed towards target acquisition, it is also aimed at locating obstacles and identifying open routes. The resulting process of recognizing, referencing and reporting minefields can be particularly difficult, due to the ease of concealment of mines and the extensive size of the mined area. Often, it is only the front edge of a minefield that can be located by ground forces and this will be hard to delineate from a distance through binoculars or a weapon sight. Should an attempt be made to approach the minefield, and gauge its limits or depth, then the defenders are likely to discourage such action with mortar and artillery fire.

If the determination of the minefield recce party reaps success in discovering the extent of the obstacle, there remains the problem of disseminating the information gained. The recce party is likely to be at the very end of the command chain and the minefield's location would be reported upwards via CNR. This entails a lengthy transmission of grid references, with the inherent possibility of mistakes arising in the passing of the message, and errors being compounded *en route*. To overcome these disadvantages, abbreviated forms of minefield reporting have been tried. One in use by British forces is based upon a clear protractor that includes a variety of shapes in varying sizes. The closest fitting shape is positioned over the outline of the minefield previously drawn on to a standard scale, military map and the co-ordinates of the protractor are noted. In this manner, the approximate shape and size of the minefield, plus its location, can be rapidly communicated by means of one set of co-ordinates and a reference to the relevant shape. Although much quicker than sending a lengthy set of six-figure grid references, the protractor method still relies upon standard CNR voice procedures and accurate repetition through the command chain.

In peacetime, it is often taken for granted that what can be achieved so easily on field training exercises can be similarly implemented in war. One example is the basic task of map reading. With the benefit of excellent road signs, up-to-date maps, military and civilian police assistance and abundant time for reconnaissance, it is rare for soldiers on field training to become badly lost. On operations, a plethora of factors accumulate to overturn the ease with which military forces expect to find their way about the battlefield. Maps are soon inaccurate as air strikes, artillery bombardment, demolitions, fire and other damage brought about in combat, change the face of the countryside. Refugees will block routes, subversives may destroy or alter road signs and freedom of movement is severely limited by the possibility of enemy action. More importantly, the soldier may find himself in completely new territory, without adequate maps and operating over terrain, such as desert or mountain, that introduces frighteningly new problems of navigation. This general difficulty compounds the concern in command posts over the actual locations of units. It also exacerbates the problem of minefield reconnaissance and reporting, since the map reference co-ordinates of the discovered obstacle cannot be given with any great certainty. Artillery units and observers faced with much the same requirement for pin-point accuracy have been provided with a variety of position fixing and navigation aids. The British computerized Position and Azimuth Detection System (PADS) was one of the first of these to be fielded, now the US forces are seeking a similar but improved capability in their Navstar Global Positioning System. It is only a small step to visualize an integrated obstacle reporting system, that is computer based with an in-built communications system. On this novel device, the integral position determining system will automatically display the computer stored map of the operator's immediate vicinity. He is then in a position to draw on to the display screen, with a light pen or mouse, the outline of the minefield or obstacle or area of contamination that he has uncovered. This system obviously has more than one role to play on the battlefield, but we will restrict discussion to its part in minefield reporting. Once the operator is satisfied that the information he has gleaned is accurately portrayed on the display, he can transmit the information as data over CNR or radio telephone trunk access to all those stations who require the details and have suitable receivers to accept it. One such recipient may be the engineer intelligence cell at divisional headquarters. The display terminal at this staff location will be receiving many similar reports which are automatically added to the computer generated battle situation map. Knowing who has equivalent facilities or not, the engineer staff can disseminate the information to those who also need it in whatever from their respective equipment can receive it. How this system works in detail is dependent upon the normal procedures adapted within the formation, the communications network, the display facilities available and the originating reconnaissance party. Combat engineers would probably feed their information up engineer channels, whilst armoured recce troops would direct their reports to formation intelligence staffs. Whatever system is employed for minefield or obstacle reporting it should be common throughout a force or an alliance. All arms need to be practised in the use of the message formats, or protractors or digitized display transmissions, which have been chosen as the methods to report mined areas promptly and accurately. It will be quite difficult enough, and consume more than an acceptable amount of time, to overcome the actual obstacle without wasting time on imprecise reporting procedures.

Monitoring and Recording

In addition to those minefields an enemy has placed in his way, or amongst his troops, a field commander will be keen to know the locations and status of those laid by his own and adjacent forces. Elaborate procedures are set up to ensure that subordinate commanders advise their superiors of intentions to lay minefields and that progress reports are issued as construction proceeds. Often, permission to lay mines may not be delegated below divisional level to ensure both central control of resources and also that less senior commanders do not inhibit the flexibility open to higher formations by closing too many manoeuvre options with restrictive minefields. As the barrier plan proceeds or the battle situation alters, the number of effective minefields will change. Some will be extended, others may be over-run or breached. At present, engineer staffs in 1st British Corps benefit from the ADP power of Wavell, which provides an easy means of storage for minefield data plus a rapid dissemination of changes to that data base amongst other Wavell terminals connected via the trunk network. But few other armed forces have a comparable system and the passage of information out of the trunk system on to CNR users continues to present problems. These result from the time and accuracy factors involved in encoding, transmitting and decoding long lists of grid references over open radio nets. Such disadvantages can be somewhat reduced if secure nets are used, protected by cryptographic equipment, or if digital message terminals are employed with burst transmission devices. Alternatively, despatch riders or liaison officers can carry marked maps or overlays about the battlefield. A very effective method of illustrating the position of minefields, whether completed, proposed or suspected, is by overprinting maps with such information. The British Army is provided with this facility by survey sections of the Royal Engineers, who operate TACIPRINT at various formation headquarters. A standard scale military map can be printed in large quantities at short notice, with a variety of new detail superimposed upon it. This is an excellent way of graphically presenting new boundaries, unit locations, obstacle details, closed routes, axes of advance and relevant combat intelligence. However, the disadvantage remains that these current and revised maps require distribution. Inevitably, only sufficient copies can be despatched in time down to unit headquarters level. Thereafter, copies have to be hand drawn within the unit to ensure that all vehicle crews, sections, officers and elements of the unit have the up-dated information to hand. Disseminating the details of the defenders' own minefields down the chain of command to the lowest level is, therefore, almost as formidable a challenge as ensuring that information on enemy obstacles is passed upwards. Technology can assist in distributing minefield information downwards by a generous allocation of digital message devices, preferably with a graphics capability. Using a trunk network/CNR interface it is feasible to transmit selected portions of a headquarters obstacle plan map display down to the units and subordinate formations in whose area the minefields are situated. This virtually instantaneous passage of digital information will be error free and common to all recipients.

Normally, it is perfectly adequate for most tactical purposes to provide the minimum of information on minefields to the majority of headquarters and units. This might simply be the location and extent of the mined area, plus a general description of the type of minefield. Engineer units and staffs will require much more than this outline. Sometimes it will be necessary to change areas of tactical responsibility between units or formations, even between forces of different nationalities. On these occasions, accurate records of minefield layouts, their contents and construction must be handed over between the outgoing and relieving units. Alternatively, it may be necessary to enter minefields in order to breach them for patrols or other operations. This is much simplified when the types of mines, numbers of rows and distances between them are known to the breaching party. And, of course, at the end of hostilities a major clearance and recovery operation must be undertaken under safe conditions when no more casualties will be acceptable. For these reasons, it is standard practice for laying units to prepare minefield records, which contain all available information on the minefield. The record is prepared in standard format, on graph paper. In this way, a scaled sketch can be drawn and supported by written detail. Regrettably, this proven and generally acceptable system of minefield recording is entirely inadequate for the modern, rapid means of delivering SM and RDM. It is possible to gauge the limits of a field sown with SM, particularly if laid from a vehicle mounted dispenser, probably less so if dropped from a helicopter. Therefore, some form of record is feasible for SM, although it may only consist of the outline shape of the mined area, the type of mines included and their quantity. For RDM it is altogether impracticable to attempt accurate recording. Mines delivered by gun, rocket or aircraft may or may not land where they were intended to, dependent upon the accuracy of the delivery system. In most circumstances the RDM will be positioned where required and confirmation of their delivery will be available from forward artillery observers or on-board weapon systems recorders for aircraft. But this can never be guaranteed, and, in the often chaotic conditions of combat, it is probably too much to expect that every SM and RDM minefield emplaced by artillery, helicopters or aircraft will be precisely referenced and lodged with the appropriate ground force operations and engineer staffs. The difficulties of recording SM and RDM are symptomatic of the control problems induced by these extremely valuable weapons. Traditionally, the decision on where mines should be laid has been a joint one, agreed between tactical and engineer commanders. Mine warfare will undoubtedly continue to be the prime responsibility of combat engineers, despite mines being available to artillery, helicopter and air force units as yet another weapon to be used against appropriate targets. It may be necessary for tactical commanders to impose restrictions of the free use of SM or RDM, to ensure that their employment does not limit his freedom of action in the future or endanger troops that cannot easily be notified of their locations. This will be a particularly complex issue across the boundary between army and air force commanders. Air force chiefs with RDM will wish to use them in battlefield interdiction tasks against an enemy in depth and possibly when called on to assist ground troops in the close air support role. Army commanders will wish to specify when and where RDM are used, to prevent their own mobility being affected, and will insist on knowing where RDM have been delivered by aircraft outside of their control. Liaison, understanding and co-operation will be essential to sensible and mutual agreements on this matter, yet history is unfortunately full of examples where army and air force accord has been severely lacking. Within an alliance the problem is aggravated by the mix of languages, differing procedures and national sensitivities. Nevertheless, the value of RDM is too great to allow their worth to be degraded by procedural impediments and the thorny issue of effective control of SM and RDM will need to be resolved. Current military communications and ADP networks can assist greatly in monitoring the diverse deployment of rapidly emplaced mines. Such C^3I systems have a major role to play in modern mine warfare and will be central to the effective utilization of increasingly expensive and potent land mines.

Automated Mine Warfare Control System

The first part of this chapter showed the extensive communications framework, which combines the sundry elements of a military force into a coherent fighting machine. The existence of this flexible and survivable, multi-path system has fostered the advent of tactical ADP equipment. Some of which, such as BATES, are extremely complex and powerful, whilst others are more limited, yet nevertheless extremely useful. Tactical message entry and read out devices fall into this latter category. Thus, the infrastructure and the equipment are available to form the basis of a computer based mine warfare command and control system. At present no such system is known to exist. A surprising fact, since the collation, monitoring, processing and display of mine information entails the handling and storage of vast amounts of data. This is exceedingly expensive in time and manpower, if attempted manually, with a high risk of error or misinterpretation arising. Just as many artillery staffs have recognized the need for ADP assistance in their specialist sphere, to ensure prompt and reactive combat support from a widely dispersed range of delivery systems with an extensive logistic tail, there is an equally apparent requirement for such aid to engineer troops and staffs. Never has this been more so than in this era of high mobility, with the ensuing demand for fast response from SM, RDM and counter-measures.

The framework for a mine warfare C^3I system will be provided by the existing communications network. The CNR grid will join individual vehicles, engineer recce parties and combat engineer sections, physically undertaking the mining and counter-measure tasks, with their commanders and headquarters. Many of these engineer staffs and commanders will be co-located with operations staffs or tactical commanders in formation headquarters. At such levels, access is gained into the trunk communications lattice, which in turn offers a multiplicity of outlets: into the logistic chain for transport, equipment and mine warfare stores; across formation boundaries for barrier liaison; into airforce nets for helicopter or fixed-wing support; into local civilian networks or back to national agencies for specialist advice. Within headquarters are the processing facilities at the heart of an automated command and control system. The computers and peripherals in the staff cells provide the central control of mine warfare activities, whilst their output through the communications network allows decentralized execution. Instructions and information can be disseminated efficiently and rapidly in data form to less complex devices at lower levels, where those responsible for taking action receive almost instantaneous, yet accurate, orders.

The central processors receive their data input by the reverse procedure. Although safeguards will be necessary, and filters will inevitably be imposed, it would be feasible for information to be supplied by the most forward engineer recce officer to the highest formation engineer staff cell, having also informed every intervening level of command, by means of a burst transmission from a digital message device. The staff computers will receive and store vast amounts of detail from a wide range of sources: engineer intelligence, combat intelligence, terrain analysis teams, meteorological stations and mine depots. This information on the weather, the ground conditions, the availability of men, vehicles, equipments and mines, and on the enemy locations, minefields and counter-measures, can be arranged, ordered, manipulated and presented with little effort, but with a great saving in time. In addition, as Intelligent Knowledge Based Systems become available, the computers will be able to offer options, recommend priorities and calculate optimum solutions to particular threats with the resources available. For the moment, the engineer staff officer would have to instruct the computer, via his terminal, to carry out a specific task on the data to provide the detail he needs. This might be: an up-to-date read out on the status of all minefields under construction; a calculation on the effectiveness, or stopping power, of a particular minefield; an assessment of mine stocks not yet committed, where they are, who is available to lay them, with what mine layers and using which transport unit. Requests from a commander or fellow staff officer for such information, late at night or in the midst of dealing with one of the hundred minor panics that arise each day, would presently be met with an inward groan, as the unfortunate recipient of the request considers the difficulties to be overcome. Firstly, he would have to leaf through paper files and signals logs to check what information is to hand, which needs updating, and which needs collecting. Having spent a considerable time on the radio or telephone to confirm or obtain the data needed, the luckless staff officer has to order his thoughts and information in a presentable fashion and carry out whatever calculations are necessary. Pleased at last with his efforts, his smile soon fades when his offered solution is rejected as being too late, or not quite what was required. The availability of an automated mine warfare control system would overcome the disadvantages of this traditional method of staff work. Not only is the staff officer released from the time-consuming drudgery of much of his current work load, but the senior staff officers and commanders receive answers to their questions much more quickly. This is as a result of the information being readily accessible or obtainable, and of the rapid computing power of modern processors. Equally, supplementary questions are answered or alternative solutions proposed with great ease and rapidity. Of special value to an engineer commander is the graphics capability offered with modern microprocessors. Mine stocks, manpower utilization and time schedules are most easily visualized when viewed as graphs or histograms, and the corresponding effects of altering any parameters are immediately apparent as the shape forms change. A graphics terminal also permits the use of digitized terrain evaluation techniques to optimize minefield layouts and locations. The introduction of computer generated map displays would also be a distinct advantage to engineer and operations cells, who need to massage resources and requirements to achieve the best tactical solution available under the prevailing conditions.

Thus, a C^3I system for mine warfare will depend initially upon a communications overlay capable of carrying data traffic. This network should allow complete connectivity between the superior headquarters containing the senior engineer field commander, and the logistic source of mines, equipment and transport, and through subordinate commands to the lowest level of combat engineer sub-unit, which undertakes the mine or counter-mine task. The communications system has to be transparent to data transmissions. The powerful processors situated at headquarters would run the necessary programs and peripherals to meet the needs of formation engineer staffs, who require visual display units with graphics capabilities, map displays, printers and plotters. Ideally, such facilities should be available at engineer battalion level too. Below the unit headquarters, tactical message devices will suffice at engineer company and platoon command posts, and for engineer recce parties.

These devices should also be provided for combat reconnaissance troops, who will be involved in the identification and reporting of enemy minefields too. There is nothing futuristic about this proposal, for the hardware, the programs and the communications equipment are available now. Indeed similar C^3I systems are being brought into service for operations, intelligence and artillery staffs. Mine warfare is no longer a staid and leisurely pursuit, to be conducted in slow time. Very expensive mines, delivery systems and counter-measures are being procured to provide the fast and responsive support that commanders of modern, mobile forces demand. Without an equally responsive command and control system, the value of new mine warfare weapons will be diminished needlessly.

9

To the Future

The Combat Effectiveness of the Mine

MINES are essentially a means of providing terrain enhancement for defensive purposes. The effect of laying mines is to improve the counter-mobility potential of a piece of ground, thereby causing an enemy to lose time, equipment and personnel. This minefield barrier results in increased protection for the defender and hence heightens the combat capability of the defending force. At the same time, mines will degrade the rate of advance of an attacker and increase the number of casualties inflicted on the assault echelon. Whilst the enemy gains less ground when mines are present, it has been shown that those defending from behind the minefield suffer fewer casualties than if no barrier were there. The presence of a minefield improves the effectiveness of the defending fire units to such an extent that a smaller force is required to hold a position than would otherwise be the case. In other words, mines contribute to the overall economy of committed, defending troops, which permits an actual increase in offensive capability by releasing forces to strengthen the mobile reserve. Extensive analysis of combat situations from World War II, the US experience in Vietnam and the 1973 Arab-Israeli War has shown that mines were second only to direct fire weapons in causing the destruction of both wheeled and tracked vehicles. An interesting detail from these studies reveals that an average of 2,000 mines were laid per vehicle casualty in World War II. (In comparison, 100,000 rounds of small arms ammunition were expended in Vietnam for every personnel casualty inflicted.) If it is remembered that modern devices are several times more effective now than were the simpler, pressure mines in use up to 1945 and that fewer are needed to inflict the same number of casualties, then mines become an even more attractive option as a defensive weapon.

The benefits to be gained from the employment of mines are many. The synergistic effect, whereby the inclusion of a minefield into a defensive position can enhance the effectiveness of the defending weapon systems by an improvement factor of between 1.5 and 2.5 is an important consideration. An ability to lay mines quickly, demonstrated on exercises and declared to be a firm intention in the preparation for war, improves the deterrent posture of a force by making an opponent believe that a surprise attack or quick advance is unobtainable. The enemy's confidence in an outcome being favourable to him is consequently reduced and the possibility of an attack correspondingly diminished. At the tactical level, mines are decidely useful on many occasions when other weapons would be impotent or impracticable. For example, they can be laid in jungle,

woods or urban areas to attack men or machines, that could otherwise avoid
detection or engagement. Equally, being unmanned, they will operate in bad
weather or extremes of climate, under artillery fire, through battlefield smoke or
dust, under conditions of enemy air superiority, and for long periods of time. They
provide the solution to a defender's concern over how he can engage the quantity
and variety of targets likely to face him in an assault wave, with the limited
number of weapons at his disposal, each of which has a fixed rate of fire. Mines
hinder an enemy's movement, extending the time of exposure and allowing each
weapon to select and engage appropriate targets in succession. This opportunity
can be gained with a very low manpower commitment, since the same party can
lay several minefields prior to the enemy closing on to the defended area. At
present, too, mines continue to hold the lead over counter-measures and cause an
enemy great inconvenience in preparing for, and attempting to, breach minefields. A further advantage of mines is that they are a passive, purely defensive
weapon. Whilst their deployment emphasizes the intent of a force or nation to
defend itself, they do not pose a threat in peace to a potential enemy or a danger to
an aggressor, unless the defended area is violated.

There should be specific objectives behind the laying of mines, and the
effectiveness of those minefields ought to be measured against the original aims.
A minefield will be designed to achieve a particular purpose, its subsequent
success being dependent upon careful siting and timely execution, in addition to
the number and types of mines it contains. Some possible uses for mines follow.
Minefields might be laid to canalize an advancing enemy force, splitting the large
formations into successively smaller groups or into selected fire zones, where they
can be dealt with by the defending elements. Those minefields placed to divert
opponents, will be aimed at changing the axis of an advance or deflecting the force
away from an important position or vital ground. Restrictive barriers are
emplaced to deny ease of manoeuvre on terrain that is otherwise negotiable
without too much effort or would be indefensible by other means. Minefields laid
to delay an enemy would be located and designed to impose a barrier to
movement, which would require a finite time to overcome. Such time could allow
reinforcements to arrive at the defending positions, or permit reserves to deploy,
or allow weapons to be brought to bear on the obstructed enemy. But a minefield
required to halt an advance might be almost unachievable, depending upon the
strength, determination and counter-measures capability of the enemy. From a
different viewpoint to that of assessing minefields in terms of counter-mobility,
mines contribute to the erosion of an opposing force's fighting strength and
momentum, improving the possibility of arranging its defeat. Destruction of a
force by mines is an unlikely occurrence, whereas the intention to destroy an
individual target by mines is entirely legitimate and feasible. However, there is an
alternative view on the utility of mines and how they should be regarded. This is
to consider the mine as a weapon of disruption rather than one to destroy discrete
targets. The concept can best be understood as a combined attack to interrupt
effective command and control, to hinder and obstruct unit and formation
manoeuvre, to inflict physical damage on men and machines, and to engender
psychological stress on commanders and soldiers alike. It is an innovative concept,
inspired by the increasing availability of SM and RDM, plus the expansion of

delivery means able to dispense them. Disruption becomes the prime objective, rather than a useful side-effect. It is a concept which must be seriously addressed, for it could have a major impact on the future role of mines in the land battle.

Current Capabilities and Limitations

It will be evident from earlier chapters that a great variety of mines are being produced, the majority of which have a general utility that recommends them for use worldwide. Yet some mines are highly specialized and may only be applicable to certain areas or situations. The shallow water, anti-amphibian mine for use on coastlines is one example, whilst the ice mine is another. The availability of a selection of counter-mine equipments leads to the conclusion that a complementary mix of mines is needed to ensure an effective defence. A traditionally-laid style of AT mine is required to form the backbone of a conventional minefield framework for a defended area. The device should preferably have an FWA capability, with inherent anti-handling and counter counter-measure properties. For use in woods or urban areas, and to reinforce minefields or close minefield lanes, ORMs are necessary. SM and RDM are the final components of the family, to provide a more rapid response to the operational demand for quickly emplaced minefields at both short and long ranges. However, there is an additional requirement for AP mines. All versions should ideally be based upon fragmentation warheads, which offer a greater casualty effect than the HE blast mines. Scatterable AP mines, deploying trip wires as they land, can be used to protect hand or mechanically laid minefields, or could be dispensed with scatterable AT mines, or be spread as nuisance mines. Similarly, AP mines can be remotely delivered to afford protection to AT mines dispensed at long range. There will, nevertheless, be an extra demand for an AP mine that can be emplaced by hand, for use in ambushes or as close protection at defended localities and battle positions. Devices and systems have been developed to meet nearly all of these needs, although few nations have a comprehensive array to match the proposals listed. Those forces which do not approach the ideal in their mine warfare capability obviously have a target to aim at, should they agree with the recommendations above. Even those armies that enjoy an excellent provision of mines and delivery systems, can not afford to be complacent, because it is unlikely that the requirements for full width, belly and track attack mines and long range, side attack mines have been adequately met at the moment. Thus, in the short term, many nations still have much to do to bring their forces up to a satisfactory position in mine warfare, before applying themselves to the needs of the future.

On the counter-measures side, there is arguably a great deal yet to be accomplished. There is currently no one state with a true counter-mine capability to meet all potential threats. Of prime concern to many will be the urgent operational requirement to clear SM and RDM, and this is the outstanding counter-measure problem of the day. Less compelling, but also important, is the desirability of perfecting an FAE system of explosive breaching, whilst flailing is a mechanical means of effecting a breach that merits much closer attention. It is unlikely that any remarkable break-through will be forthcoming on mine counter-measures, the immediate future must be devoted to improving those means that already exist and combining them into a harmonized family of counter-mine equipments. Even less advanced than counter-measures are mine warfare command and control systems. A determined effort is called for to standardize and automate the diverse procedures, which are used throughout formations, armies and alliances to direct mine and counter-mine operations. The communications exist and the electronic devices are available to be consolidated into a control system capable of multiplying the total effectiveness of a force's mine warfare capability. Yet the logical steps to organize these capricious arrangements into methodical order and automate the resultant system have not been taken. Undoubtedly, this oversight will be corrected as digital communications networks, computers and associated peripheral devices become more commonplace and acceptable in the combat zone. Although there is much to be done to bring the majority of armed forces up to a standard in mine warfare that is both desirable and practical within the restraints of modern military technology, it would be inadvisable to limit aspirations to what is the perceived requirement today. For the situation is never stationary. Circumstances are ever changing, for example the whole context can be radically altered by a re-alignment of political views or the adoption of a new military doctrine. Technology can offer new opportunities to influence requirements too, but the most decisive spur to an adjustment in military capability is the perception of a new or modified threat.

Threat Development

It is apparent that there is a worldwide trend to increase the number of AFVs in armed forces. Reconnaissance vehicles, command posts, air defence weapons, personnel carriers, rocket launchers and artillery pieces are all being produced in armoured versions, often on tracked chassis. Thus, the hard target is becoming the normal target. And the combat potential of each of those targets is increasing, which is why armoured protection is being provided to them. For instance, APCs are being replaced by IFVs with integral anti-armour weapons. Equally, it is no longer easy to specify the relative importance of, say, a command post or surface to air missile system when compared to an MBT. The latter may continue to have a leading position on the battlefield, but it is difficult to say by how much it predominates. The conclusion to be drawn must be that the current inclination to optimize AT mines for the defeat of MBT can not continue unchallenged. It would be wrong to remain mesmerized by the tank threat, when the target array contains an equal number of high value targets that current mines do not attack. This is often the case, since many AT fuzes are tuned to ignore all but the prime MBT target. On pressure mines, this is simply a matter of calibrating the pressure sensor to react only when the measured impulse corresponds to that of a suitably heavy vehicle. Many other tracked vehicles have a much lower ground bearing pressure than MBT and can pass over AT mines with impunity. Similarly, influence sensors will respond to targets that fit into a narrow, detection window and signals from enemy vehicles that fall outside this preferred band will be ignored. Perhaps the first step in opening up their potential use is to change the name of this type of mine from anti-tank to anti-armour. Although the price of intelligent fuzed, anti-armour mines is greater than in the past, they do remain a reasonably inexpensive weapon. It seems illogical to lay or deliver many of these in the full knowledge that they will deliberately avoid detonation below anything other than their principal tank target. As valuable a contribution to the erosion of the combat potential of an all arms formation can be made by damaging or destroying a variety of vehicles, as by the exclusive targeting of MBT. Indeed, the present desirability of reducing the initiation threshold of AT mines may ultimately become a necessity. Two factors suggest this. The first is the availability of weapon systems such as the Commando Stingray and the development of even lighter tanks, for example ELKE. The Stingray is a compact tank, made of Cadloy armour with a very low ground pressure of 0.7 kg/cm. Yet it has the punch of an MBT with its 105-millimetre main armament. Such a powerful gun platform could traverse many AT minefields in relative safety especially as its excellent mobility (top speed 40 mph) would enable it to travel at speeds that the alerter sensors on AT mines would register as too high to be of interest. The ELKE (Elevated Kinetic Energy Weapon System) light tank, comprising an externally mounted 75-millimetre gun on an M551 chassis, would also have a sufficiently low ground pressure to raise doubts over the effectiveness of normal AT mine fuzes against it. Evidently, a new range of modified anti-armour fuzes is required that will deal with these light, fast weapon platforms, which, nevertheless, have the firepower and destructive potential of MBT.

The second factor necessitating a review of mine fuze response levels is the possibility that all future MBT will be lighter and faster than they are now. The US Tank Automotive Command (TACOM) has sponsored a programme aimed at developing a more survivable MBT based on new components and technology. This initiative has arisen from their conviction that survivability can no longer be assured by adding more armour to a tank. Some means of reducing the protected volume of an MBT is required. Currently the whole hull and turret must be surrounded by heavy armour, with the ensuing size and weight problems. A similar attitude to the need to reduce the silhouette of MBT is evident in West Germany and amongst Soviet tank designers. The German authorities believe that Leopard 2 represents the ultimate shape for a tank of the classical form and that the design limits have now been reached. Open source reports on design options for the Soviet T90 also indicate that they are considering a severe reduction in the size of the turret, by placing all crew positions within the hull. The trend, therefore, seems to be towards a turretless MBT, or externally mounted gun concept as it is sometimes called. A reduction in the silhouette alone will make the tank more survivable, but this is also improved by the higher mobility that the lighter, turretless tank can achieve. Higher MBT speeds across open ground, where minefields might typically be placed, will mean that mine fuzes must be reprogrammed to attack faster targets than before. Alternatively, the weight of armour saved from removing the turret might be redistributed to provide higher protection for the hull. This would lead to belly and side attack mines having to penetrate much thicker armour than they face now, with a consequent need for improved warheads.

One potential change to the conventional design of MBT, that should have no detrimental effect on the utility of present mines, is the placing of tank engines to the front of the hull. The Israeli Merkava tank is the only MBT in service so configured, but it is known that the West Germans examined this possibility as recently as 1983 with their VTF experimental vehicle. In such a design the most vulnerable part of the tank should remain the mid-third, which is where influence and side attack mines tend to be targeting today. The benefit of positioning the power pack forward is that frontal protection is increased, since anti-armour projectiles or HEAT jets must penetrate the whole engine compartment before attacking the crew area. Improving tank protection in this way makes it more difficult for direct fire weapons to engage MBT in assault formation, which makes it even more important to protect defensive positions with mines capable of attacking the tank's side, tracks or belly. The reported concern over the vulnerability of AFVs to top attack may lead to concerted efforts to increase the thickness of top armour. Should this arise it will not have a major effect on mines, other than to suggest that the development of top attack mines may not be a profitable design route to follow. However, the introduction of appliqué or explosive armour kits is one development, which does have an impact on contemporary ORM. The side attack of AFVs protected by appliqué armour will be decidedly more difficult, demanding either more powerful HEAT warheads or an attack mechanism not susceptible to the disruptive effect of explosive armour.

A new word has entered the jargon of the AFV design and development community recently. With a similar meaning to avionics it is vetronics, standing for vehicle electronics. The electronics systems in modern MBT have now become so extremely complex that they rival those of combat aircraft. Vetronics, therefore, covers the science and technology of electronics applied to vehicles allowing for the total integration of their electrical, electronic and optronic systems. Elements of this integrated whole would include communications, fire control, stabilization, navigation, engine control, NBC protection and air conditioning. Ultimately, it is hoped that computerization and automatic analysis of the information being gleaned by advanced surveillance and target acquisition will be incorporated into vetronics systems, along with the use of artificial intelligence and robotics. At this point, the role of the human crew will be much diminished and their numbers reduced. Nevertheless, well before this situation is reached the importance of vetronics to tank performance will have reached a critical level. In the more advanced MBT, such as Challenger and Abrams, this level may have been reached already. Their sophisticated gun sights and fire control systems are computer driven and achieve very high probabilities of first-round hits on moving targets. This dependence on vetronics amongst new and future MBT points to an area of vulnerability that could be exploited by the next generation of AT mines. Rather than attacking the tracks or crew of an AFV, the prime target could become the electronic control systems, which permit the tank to move and fight. By dislocating the devices and associated circuits needed to locate, track and engage targets, the tank's potency is destroyed and its combat value negated. If the vital functions of an MBT are to be concentrated into electronic systems, then those systems must logically become a justifiable target for attack. How disruption of the vetronics is to be achieved must wait for much closer attention to be paid to this form of attack in future development programmes.

An increasing threat, which has been underestimated widely despite its significance, is that from the armed helicopter. Yet there are many examples of its utility in battle. The employment by US forces of Bell Cobra gunships in Vietnam has received considerable publicity and their effectiveness has been praised by those fortunate enough to have experienced fire support from them. Another American helicopter, the Hughes 500, has also been used on operations, this time in the service of the Israeli Defence Forces. During the 1982 invasion of Lebanon, Israeli pilots flying 500 MD variants were credited with several kills against Syrian tanks. More recently Mi–24 Hind attack helicopters have been flown under combat conditions both by the Soviets in Afghanistan and the Iraquis in the Gulf War. Indeed, the extent of Soviet helicopter operations in Afghanistan has firmly established the value of rotary wing aircraft in difficult terrain and weather. Years of tactical and logistic experience have been gained by the Soviet forces as a result of their helicopter activities in Afghanistan, and much of their expertise is relevant to attack helicopter operations. There have been several recent developments in Soviet tactical thinking on the use of helicopters, possibly as a result of Afghanistan experience. For example, there is now an Army Aviation branch responsible for helicopter operations at the tactical level and an air-ground assault group concept has been formulated to add an additional dimension to their attack options. Recognizing the value of armed helicopters, the Soviets have placed greater emphasis on the need to defeat enemy helicopters, insisting on anti-helicopter defences being as effective as anti-tank measures. A measure of their concern is shown in the belief that helicopter anti-armour ambushes could offer benefits in the order of 4 to 1. This means that an armed helicopter could kill up to 4 tanks in one sortie before withdrawing safely to re-arm and re-fuel, after which several more similar sorties could be repeated. Computerized wargames suggest that one anti-tank helicopter could account for between 15 and 20 AFVs before itself becoming a casualty.

Some helicopters, such as the UK Lynx equipped with TOW, are specifically intended for the attack of armour. Guided on to a suitable target array of enemy AFVs by a recce helicopter, a team of these specialist anti-tank aircraft would hover in an ambush position, perhaps behind a tree-line or high buildings, then a simultaneous attack by all helicopters firing repeated salvoes of ATGW would wreak havoc through the surprise and shock of the violent action. The advanced sights available and the range of missiles allow engagements to take place at distances of several kilometres. Vehicles being engaged by helicopters at these ranges find it extremely difficult to detect their attackers, and even when located there are few weapons capable of retaliating. Other armed helicopters have a mix of weapons, including ATGW, rockets and cannon. These aircraft can attack a wide variety of targets and might be employed as escorts for a heliborne assault group. Providing suppressive fire support for the landing troops, these modern gunships are effective against trenches, bunkers, buildings and AFVs. Unlike a tank, which can be hunted by men on foot with cheap, short-range weapons, the armed helicopter is virtually invulnerable to the usual cross-section of weapons available to tank or infantry companies. The successful engagement of attack helicopters is dependent upon air defence cannon and missiles being brought to bear. The Bofors RBS 70 Ray Rider is one such special purpose, anti-helicopter missile system using laser guidance to reach targets out to 5 kilometres. This, and similar weapons, require dedicated vehicles and tend to be expensive devices, resulting in a very limited distribution. Consequently, an alternative means of deterring or defeating armed helicopters is required, that can be issued on a more liberal basis than current air defence weapons.

Unfortunately, the attack helicopter is becoming an ever more difficult target to defeat. The Hind is already a formidable weapons platform, yet Soviets are planning to replace it in the early 1990s with an improved and updated aircraft, the Mi–28 Havoc. In the West, a modern anti-tank helicopter has been produced by Italy in the form of the Agusta A129 Mangusta, whilst France and Germany are collaborating in the development of a totally new range of combat helicopters. However, the most important programme, in terms of cost, size and complexity, has been the Apache AH–64A project. Hughes Helicopters, the prime contractor to the US Army for the aircraft, understandably claim that the Apache is built for battle. It is the world's most advanced attack helicopter, capable of unlimited operations in darkness and bad weather. With twin engines powering it up to speeds of 200 mph, the Apache employs laser, IR and TV technologies to acquire and track targets for its extensive range of armaments. These include Hellfire anti-armour missiles, 2.75 in rocket pods, a 30-millimetre chain gun and Sidewinder air-to-air missiles. Its passive defences are based upon radar jammers, IR flares, a very low detectability cross-section, and crew compartment armour shielding. Altogether, the Apache is a unique and impressive trend-setter, highly survivable and very lethal. But its excellence is achieved at an equally impressive price, and its imitators will be just as costly. Also expensive are the new generation of troop-lift and utility helicopters, such as the US Black Hawk and Anglo-French Super Puma. These aircraft are built for effectiveness, performance and survivability too. Thus the threats to ground forces from rapid heliborne assault or devastating stand-off attack are multiplying, and defending troops urgently require an inexpensive counter. This could take the form of an anti-helicopter mine.

There is a precedent for the anti-aircraft mine, which arose during World War II, when Luftwaffe attacks threatened the cities of Great Britain. Two versions of the device were produced, the Short and the Long Aerial Mine. Both were intended to defeat mass bomber raids by disrupting the flying formation, through the deployment of heavy steel wires suspended from parachutes. Whilst this may no longer be the optimum solution, it indicates the feasibility of a mine being a suitable counter-measure to the helicopter. One modern equivalent to World War II devices is the Wallop Industries Skysnare. This is a remotely activated kite balloon, which can be made to rise rapidly to a height of 300 metres. The Kevlar tethering cable is an obstacle to low flying aircraft and forces them up higher, where they are more vulnerable to air defence missiles and guns. The anti-helicopter mine would also be a pre-positioned weapon to deny transit routes, landing zones or fire positions to the enemy's helicopters. Just as a field commander will make an appreciation of the terrain to deduce how enemy ground forces could approach or assault his defensive positions, it will be possible to decide where a helicopter mobile force would wish to land to attack him, what routes helicopters would prefer to use to infiltrate his area of tactical responsibility, and which features armed helicopters would hover behind to fire at his troops. Once the most dangerous of these options have been assessed it would be possible to sow the respective areas with anti-helicopter mines, just as the most suitable locations for AT and AP minefields are selected and prepared. It should also be borne in mind that combat helicopters favour contour or Nap-of-the-Earth flying to avoid detection by air defence radars. The aircraft fly so low and close to the ground, following the natural features, and shielding themselves with woods, buildings and hillsides, that they are well within range of ground emplaced SFF or plate charge warheads. Equally, acoustic, MMW and IR sensors are now available, that are quite capable of detecting helicopters and being incorporated in anti-helicopter mine fuzes. The helicopter threat must no longer be neglected. Many nations are investing considerable resources into developing rotary-wing aircraft that are potent weapon platforms, with firepower and mobility above those of the tank. A positive and generally available means of defence is required against these modern machines, that will otherwise create havoc amongst ground troops. Expensive, missile and quick-firing cannon air defence systems will never be so widely issued as to present a credible response to the Apache or the Mi-28 type of aircraft. Accordingly, anti-helicopter mines must be considered as an urgent operational requirement in order to reduce the present superiority that attack helicopters have over ground forces, and to counter the threat of heliborne assault.

Concepts and Doctrine

Although many weapons are developed as a response to a particular threat, and perceived danger provides the greatest impetus to procurement, there are other factors having a major influence on weapon concepts. For example, the growth of urban areas is an unmistakable trend in many parts of the world. It is particularly noticeable in the Central Region of NATO, where major centres of population are ever expanding with a consequent reduction in the amount of rural land. Serving this proliferation of industrial estates, suburbs and dormitory villages is an extensive road network, offering the very fastest routes for any would-be invader. Rather than struggling across open pastures or crop fields, true to the popular image of advancing armoured formations, an aggressor could choose to follow the excellent, well-signed motorways and roads from town to town. Such a tactic would require a different mine warfare response from that currently planned by most nations. A shift in emphasis would be required away from patterned minefields laid by conventional mine layers to an increased dependence upon ORM for use in built-up areas and to deny routes. Thus, a change in the environment will cause a revision to weapon requirements, as will new deployment or organizational concepts.

A recent development in force structures has been the renewed interest shown in rapid deployment forces. Britain has reconstituted its airborne capability in the form of a parachute brigade and France has formed the Force d'Action Rapide (FAR). This latter formation consists of paratroop, air-mobile and light armoured forces capable of being transported 1000 kilometres a day to any part of the globe where French interests are to be defended. Incidents in the Middle East and

Central America, plus actual combat in Grenada, have reinforced American determination to form a true Rapid Deployment Force (RDF), now known as the US Central Command. An indication of their progress in this venture is the formation of the US Army's Light Infantry Division. Organized to engage in low to mid intensity operations and deploy quickly anywhere in the world, the divisions are equipped on light scales. Inevitably, these, and similar, forces must be prepared for operations almost immediately upon arrival. They will have to contend with the situation as they find it, and hold the ring. Usually, the most dangerous period for an intervention force is during the initial deployment, before the formation is up to strength and support weapons have been unloaded. It is then that the lightly-equipped units are most vulnerable. If the indigenous foe has AFVs or MBTs the danger is greater and may not be diminished even when the heavier weapons are to hand. A traditional method of enhancing the defences of infantry when faced by more powerful or mobile forces is to use protective minefields. However, rapid deployment forces can not carry substantial quantities of conventional mines or easily provide the means of mechanical laying. The limited numbers of mines that could be provided must be used precisely and with economy. For this reason, SM or RDM appear to be most suited to the needs of light divisions and air-transportable units. Wheeled vehicles tend to be used in support of these formations, on a scale which is far from generous, however, some could be equipped with dispensers for the rapid laying of SM. Alternatively, helicopters could be used, but these too are often in rare supply. But one means of delivering mines accurately and rapidly can be proposed. This is the use of 120-millimetre mortars with cargo shells containing minelets. The Thomson-Brandt rifled mortar is able to project its 120 RT 61 carrier rounds out to 8 kilometres, at a high rate of fire, from a weapon which is both lighter and cheaper than equivalent howitzers. Mortars are traditional infantry weapons and provide battalion commanders with their own, integral fire support. They come highly recommended as immediate and reponsive weapons, which the infantryman has learned to trust. The provision of a 120-millimetre shell will considerably enhance the utility of mortars, and increase their value to rapid deployment forces.

For most of the NATO nations, the focus of alliance defence remains the Central Region, where the strength of Warsaw Pact land forces appears to pose the greatest threat. Two developments in tactical doctrine for this area have recently arisen, which could precipitate significant changes in mine warfare capabilities. One results from the NATO Defence Planning Council decision of 9 November 1984 to adopt a strike-deep doctrine, officially identified as Follow On Force Attack, or FOFA. Briefly, this envisages a firm defence at the FEBA to resist and hold an initial assault, whilst enemy second and third echelons are attacked along with bridges, railways and airfields well to the enemy's rear. The central idea is to delay the approach of Soviet reserves, which would otherwise be brought into battle much earlier, quicker and in larger numbers than those of NATO. Adopting the FOFA doctrine is designed to gain time and build up force strengths by impeding the advance of Warsaw Pact reserve echelons and throwing their highly complicated approach plan into confusion. It is not a new operational concept, in the past it was known as battlefield interdiction or depth attack, but military technology has advanced to such an extent that renewed emphasis can be placed on the doctrine. Mobile columns can be added to the potential target list now, in addition to the former static ones. FOFA can start as little as 30 kilometres from the forward battle zone and extend as far as reconnaissance assets and weapon systems permit. The key elements of this concept are disruption and delay, which are very suitable tasks for the mine. It follows that RDM, dispensed by missile and aircraft, should play a significant part in FOFA. Systems already exist that fit the doctrine nicely: the German AT2 mine delivered by MLRS (Multi Launch Rocket System) will cause disarray amongst armoured columns, just as the British JP233 air-delivered weapon will deny airfields and railway junctions. But there is scope for additional mine systems to be procured to meet the demands of FOFA, an important tactical doctrine which has provided the incentive for future work on depth attack weapons.

The second development within NATO with a resultant impact on mine technology has been the United States acceptance of the Airland Battle doctrine. Unlike FOFA, which is a guideline for NATO wide action, Airland Battle is a purely national interpretation of the US Army's Field Manual 100–5 Operations directive to maintain the spirit of offence whilst conducting a defence. The enemy has to be denied the opportunity to exploit superior numbers at the time and place of his choosing. He must be attacked throughout the depth of his force to reduce his ability to concentrate an effective combat mass at any critical time or location. The intention is to turn the enemy commander on to the defensive, to make him react to, not initiate, combat action. In 1982, the US Defense Secretary Caspar Weinberger proposed an extension of this doctrine as a new operational concept for NATO to take it into the next century. Known as Airland Battle 2000, it has generated considerable debate and remains under discussion. Secretary Weinberger's main theme was to exploit the potential of emerging technologies available in the West to counter the numerical and positional superiority of the Warsaw Pact forces. Yet the document presented at the NATO ministerial meeting in December 1982 went farther than this, to note that US forces must be prepared to fight almost anywhere in the world and that technology must be used to gain not only a combat advantage but also provide strategic mobility. Annexes to the document presented futuristic weapon options to allow divisional commanders the ability to reconnoitre out to 150 kilometres and influence the battle out to 70 kilometres, with assets available to the corps commanders exceeding these distances. Several proposals were directly relevant to mine warfare. RPVs for example, would no longer be used exclusively to obtain information, as their payload could be increased to include an on-board attack mechanism. The weapon load might usefully comprise mines that could be dispensed from the RPV on command of the ground controller, to harass enemy forces detected by the RPV sensors. Alternatively, there is an emerging technology programme that is under way and already employs mines. The Sense and Destroy Armour (SADARM) project is based upon carrier projectiles delivered by the 8-inch cannon, with sub-munitions that include the ERAM (extended range anti-armour munition) mine. ERAM is probably the most ambitious mine system ever to be considered, depending as it does on a double SFF warhead, intelligent fuzed, area defence weapon concept. It is intended that, after landing, the mine's acoustic antennae will detect approaching vehicles. The fuze microprocessor will compute the target speed and direction, firing one of the IR seeking, top-attack warheads over the enemy vehicle at its predicted location. ERAM can also be delivered in the US Air Force SUU-65 Tactical Munitions Dispenser, out to the maximum range of the parent aircraft. This is obviously a high technology project using the very latest sensor, signal processing and warhead development and fits readily into the Airland Battle 2000 concept. Also mentioned for consideration was the use of air-cushion vehicles to overcome barriers. There is much to recommend hovercraft as counter-measure vehicles in view of their minimal ground pressure and low magnetic signature. Pressure and magnetic fuzed mines would be of limited value against hovercraft, which could traverse minefields towing explosive clearance hoses behind them. So far, air-cushion vehicles have not been investigated in any great detail as components of land counter-measure systems. This may well change in the future as the value of these lightweight amphibians becomes more apparent, both in the area of mine counter-measures and as a highly suitable RDF vehicle. Whilst Airland Battle doctrine has been assimilated into US Army teaching, and complements the FOFA objectives supported by the rest of NATO, the extrapolation of its themes into the weapon systems envisaged by Airland Battle 2000 will not be easy. By their very nature, these weapons will entail considerable technical risk and expense. Yet this may be the price that the more advanced, industrialized nations have to pay in order to maintain an effective defence in the future.

Technical Opportunities

Undoubtedly, the greatest opportunities for improvements in mine warfare, as in most other military and industrial spheres, will arise through the medium of electronic engineering. Advances in sensor technology are already in evidence and this trend will continue. Indeed, the spur provided by the US programme concerned with Sensor Fuzed Munitions has resulted in commendable progress, both in the application of passive sensors and of the more active target seekers. A new term has been mooted of late, the super sensor, which is a combination of MMW radar and passive IR. Oblivious to weather and most counter-measures, the super sensor could be a fundamental component of third generation mines, with particular relevance to RDM and ORM. As important to mines as sensors, are the digital signal processing properties of the fuze. Many extraneous and misleading signals will be detected by the sensors, such that extensive filtering of the input is required before the necessary output can be offered to the microprocessor for analysis. And this analysis has to be completed in a fraction of a second, if a fast moving target is to be engaged accurately by the mine. Thus the capacity and speed of microprocessors will play a vital role in the mine of the future. The powerful partnership of sensors and microprocessors has been exploited in the US ERAM mine mentioned earlier and will provide the basis of the proposed German mine, known as Lasso. This is a self-contained AT device, which can be laid by hand, or mechanically or remotely. It would lie in wait until its acoustic alerter sensor warned of an approaching target. Once the micro-processor has assessed it to be a worthwhile target, and within the mine's lethal area, the self-erecting warhead would be raised into attack mode, facing the general direction of the target. Range measurement and tracking of the target takes place until the microprocessor can compute a suitable lead angle and bearing for the warhead. When this is achieved, the weapon is fired.

Both ERAM and Lasso are under development, being entirely feasible with present technology. Anticipated progress in sensing and microprocessing, plus the parallel improvements in robotics, onboard machine intelligence, and RPV technology open up even greater possibilities. On the counter-measures side, small unmanned vehicles have a long and successful record in dealing with terrorist devices. Remotely-controlled bulldozers are available worldwide and could be used in mine clearance, or their control systems might be adapted for use on flail, roller or plough tanks. These are all achievable with well proven components and radio command links, however, artificial intelligence will add an entirely new dimension to unmanned vehicle capabilities. The US Defense Advanced Research Projects Agency has started a programme recently to develop an autonomous robot land vehicle, for employment in areas that are particularly hazardous to human operators. The 8×8 test bed vehicle will be entirely self-contained, quite independent of human control. TV cameras, lasers and radar sensors feed data into the vehicle's control computer (or inference engine) which determines the route to be taken to avoid obstacles. Advanced computer architectures, artificial intelligence, robotic techniques and sensory perception technologies are contributing to this Martin Marietta Aerospace development, scheduled for completion in 1989. Such a vehicle has several applications in mine warfare, from mine detection through minefield reconnaissance to lane breaching, and deserves close attention by those responsible for counter-mine operations. Yet the very same, highly complicated technologies and control systems can be used to enhance the lethality of mines, rather than diminish the threat from them. Ranger, for example, is another US development, but is a remotely-controlled, mobile mine. Linked to its operator by an optic fibre cable, Ranger is a small, highly manoeuvrable, four-wheeled vehicle with excellent off-road mobility, and carries an anti-armour, shaped charge warhead. Ranger is very low and can be driven into the rear or side of a tank, or below the front glacis plate for a virtual belly attack. The speed of the vehicle is sufficiently superior to that of any tank as to allow it to pursue and overtake most AFVs, to press home an attack. For the more distant, remote attack of AFVs, it has been proposed that an RPV be the platform for an anti-armour warhead. Named Helkath by the US Army Ballistic Laboratory, this disposable, automated device could be the first of the "brilliant", rather than "smart", third generation mines. After a simple, assisted launch, the RPV cruises to its predetermined landing area, which may be as distant as 55 kilometres. Following the controlled, crash landing, Helkath becomes an entirely independent and completely autonomous mine with an attack radius in excess of 500 metres. Developed for use in open country, Helkath will use a mix of sensors to detect and acquire its target. Initially, the system is alerted by an acoustic sensor and a small rocket is ignited to power the RPV mine towards the target at ground level. An electro-optic seeker locks on to the moving AFV, causing the mine to home into and collide with its target, much as the Ranger does. With an integral anti-handling capability, Helkath is well suited for employment in the airfield denial role or for the attack of helicopter operating bases. Representing, as it does, an innovative use of many modern techniques, Helkath is a particularly good example of what could be achieved in mine warfare by exploiting technical opportunities provided by electronics technology. Yet there is another area, in which further improvements to the mine may be possible.

Mine warhead technology is in need of a thorough re-appraisal to determine where future research and development is likely to be most beneficial. It has been noted earlier, that the vulnerability of the MBT, and to a lesser extent the attack helicopter, is being centred more on the optical and electronic system than on the crew. Thus, warheads which penetrate the hull and neutralize the tank control systems or which explode externally and shatter an MBT's optics and sensors could achieve kills as satisfactory as those that arise from crew injuries. Alternatively, the less well protected engine compartment may become the future target for attack. Improvements in crew compartment protection, from reactive and appliqué armours for example, make attacks on the fighting compartment ever more difficult. On the other hand, MBT power packs are becoming more complex as greater demands are placed on the main engine. Attacking this concentrated and complicated array of pipes, leads, joints, sensors and precision components could produce a profitable return by rendering the target immobile, denying its major source of power, and giving rise to fuel fires. However, the pressing need in warhead technology is to provide a true, full width capability, that is effective against both belly and track. Possible solutions might lie in a mine containing several sub-warheads, or linear shaped charges being employed in favour of the present conical ones. Whatever the solution, the provision of an FWA warhead must be a high priority in future projects.

Future Mine Concepts

New threats, contemporary operational plans or novel technologies may induce changes in mine warfare, just as the need to resist counter-measures will also instigate mine developments. The form and extent of such developments will be limited by several factors. Predominantly amongst these will be lethality, not simply to meet the current threat, but to include a capacity for enhancement as the target alters. Any new mine system will have to meet the response times and laying rates demanded by operational commanders too. In addition, there will be an inevitable desire to minimize the logistic burden that future mines place upon the combat services. The effective counter-measures that future mines must be designed to resist include both explosive and mechanical equipments. In particular, FAE, mine ploughs and flails are those devices with the greatest counter-mine potential. To avoid destruction by the heavy flail chains or the explosive power of FAE it will be necessary to bury mines deeper than they are laid at present. Deep buried mines will also defeat the efforts of ploughs to lift them out of the ground, if the mines are sown deeply enough. Rapid laying at greater depth will, of course, present practical problems which will require great inventiveness to overcome. Alternative approaches might be to place greater emphasis on anti-disturbance fuzes to attack ploughs and rollers, or to manufacture tougher mine cases to withstand explosive clearance, or to increase the size of mines, such that a detonation induced by a counter-measure will destroy both the counter-measure and the parent vehicle. These options and many more will, no doubt, be examined by military research establishments and mine manufacturers across the world. A special effort is likely to be made within NATO, if a US proposal is accepted to consider the Improved Conventional Mine System (ICOMS) as a candidate for collaboration within the Research and Development Industry Incentive Test Programme. The difficulties of developing a third generation mine with intrinsic resistance to counter-measures, that can be laid at the high rates of delivery demanded by operational users, should not be underestimated. The expense and complexity of this undertaking suggest that international co-operation could be essential if an effective solution is to be found, and ICOMS may well be the ideal vehicle for such collaboration.

A completely different answer to counter-measures would be to avoid them. This could be achieved by increased investment in ORM, which attack breaching parties from off the line of the breach. Current ORM are omni-directional and tend to be sited to cover tracks, gaps in hedge-lines or other obvious routes. To dominate an area, and deny easy passage as effectively as a conventional minefield, the future ORM has to increase its field of view and lethal area. ERAM and Lasso have gone some way towards meeting this requirement, but farther advances in Area Defence Weapons (ADW) are needed. A device is required which can be manually or mechanically emplaced with the minimum of effort. It will also need to be very powerful, as it is likely to engage targets from any angle: front, side or rear. In addition to being potent and simple to operate, the ADW must also have a superior fuze, since it will be required to detect, track and engage its targets within a very wide arc, perhaps up to a complete 6400 mils (360°). There are many possibilities of mine configuration that could meet this sort of operational demand, the most obvious being a LAW type missile on a turntable, with a command link to a suitable sensor/fuze assembly. Other concepts could include a multi-faced, horizontal SFF warhead or vertically-launched, short range, top attack missiles. The number of options is only limited by the imagination of the designer, as the component technologies are available today. The introduction of ADWs must simply wait for the stimulus of an agreed military requirement and its associated funding. Just as an FWA fuze increases the lethal radius of a mine and enhances the effect of any minefield in which it is laid, the adoption of ADW would offer equally significant improvements in barrier effectiveness. The footprint of an ADW is considerably greater than that for any other mine, since the ground dominated by the device could be as much as the circular area swept out by a radius equivalent to the engagement range of the sensor-warhead. Thus, far fewer ADW than conventional mines are needed to provide the same obstacle. This is as well, for ADW will be relatively expensive in comparison with the unit price of present day mines, but this is an unfair juxtaposition. The ADW will be so advanced technically, that it would be better to contrast it with an ATGW. Indeed, this approach should be taken when assessing the cost implications of all future mines, mines that are becoming more lethal, more effective and consequently better value for money, although their individual price has risen.

The same arguments for resistance to mechanical and explosive counter-measures, which point to the need to bury mines deeper than at present in order to protect them with a thick layer of earth, also suggest that an unusual form of mining should be resurrected from the past. A form that is easy to conceal and quick to put into effect. This potential panacea is the pipe mine. The technique was developed in the United Kingdom during 1941 to prepare airfields for denial, should a German invasion be attempted from the air. Pipes were buried below the surface of runways or taxiways and filled with explosives. Unfortunately, the recovery and removal of these pre-filled metal tubes was a major, sometimes dangerous, task in the years following World War II, when the airfields and surrounding areas had to be rendered safe. A more acceptable option in peacetime is to lay empty pipes in those areas where mining, anti-armour ditching, runway denial, abutment demolition or cratering may be required in war. Modern pipe-laying techniques can be quick and inexpensive, using flexible, plastic tubing and the well-proven methods of cable or drain laying. These defensive preparations have a minimal effect on the environment, as the disturbed ground soon grows over, returning to its original state and blending in smoothly with the surroundings. Thus, empty pipes can be laid in peace during a time of tension and filled quickly with a liquid explosive when their use is imminent. Most industrial pumps and tankers would suffice as the means of delivering liquid explosive, such as Astrolite or Nitromethane, with the minimum of modification. Alternative explosives, with the necessary fluid properties, could be FAE and slurry or emulsion based mixtures. There is much to recommend pipe mines as components of a defensive barrier, being inconspicuous, cheap, entirely passive, and safe until charged with explosive filling. They are particularly suitable for use on borders and frontiers, separating potentially hostile neighbours, although their benefits are equally obvious in the denial of major roads or open expanses of farmland. Pipe mines could be an extremely versatile, low cost, low risk, low technology solution to the requirement for rapid barrier emplacement. Buried months or years in advance, filled when the situation demands, and detonated at once, or remotely, or by an influence fuze, the pipe mine is flexible and responsive. It is surprising that this simple system, with so much to offer, has not been developed or adopted to any extent. Perhaps the recent US Army interest in its application may well engender the greater attention that this concept deserves.

The future may also bring novel means of delivering mines, in addition to the new devices themselves. As noted earlier, SM tend to be scattered in the local vicinity of the dispenser, whilst RDM are delivered at some considerable distance from both the releasing authority and the point of origin of the delivery system. Between these two extremes, there is often no capability to lay mines, yet a requirement to do so exists. The success of SM is dependent upon timely intelligence on enemy movement to allow an obstacle to be placed in their way. The location chosen for the minefield will always be based upon an element of risk, since the enemy may change direction and avoid the SM barrier. Equally, RDM are normally delivered to an area where it is anticipated that an enemy might be, or where it is known that they were. To overcome such uncertainties a means of delivery is required that will place the mines in front of or amidst the actual targets. A Direct Delivery Mine (DDM) is needed. The mine itself could take the form of almost any SM or RDM, but the delivery system will be a virtual direct fire weapon. The range of delivery should be the maximum distance that a ground observer can normally see, perhaps 2 kilometres. The type of delivery system is open to debate, but might be tank main armament (120-millimetre or 125-millimetre calibre barrels could deliver effective belly attack mines), demolition guns (the UK AVRE 165-millimetre barrel appears ideally suited for this task), or compressed air mortars. Although it could be argued that RDM fired from artillery can meet the requirement to engage targets some 1 or 2 kilometres ahead of defensive positions, this would seem to waste the potential range capability of artillery, that could otherwise be attacking the enemy in greater depth. On the other hand, a local, shorter range DDM under the direct control of the immediate ground commander will be extremely responsive to the tactical situation and bolster the anti-armour defences of that battle position. Another neglected means of mine delivery is the tactical transport aircraft. Helicopters have been considered and used for dispensing of SM, despite their limited load carrying capacity. The larger, rotary wing aircraft, such as the Boeing Chinook, could be employed in this role and have the capacity to deliver huge quantities of mines. However, heavy-lift helicopters are a very scarce resource, in constant demand, that may have to be used on tasks for which only they are suited. The need to lay large numbers of SM, very rapidly, could be met by adopting utility transport aeroplanes. These aircraft are specifically designed to have a large capacity and an ability to fly low and slowly. The Lockheed Hercules, Britten-Norman Defender or Shorts Skyvan all meet this requirement. It is not proposed, however, that they should compete with attack aircraft, capable of delivering mines deep into enemy territory. Rather, a tactical transport aircraft would sow large minefields in a very short time within friendly-held areas, perhaps to seal off an exposed flank or to emplace a deep obstacle ahead of a dangerous enemy breakthrough. Helicopters and vehicle mounted dispensers can not compete with the laying rates that could be achieved by dispensers mounted within transport airframes, dispersing mines through the wide cargo doors. In some areas of the world, where vehicle movement is slow or helicopters find difficulty in operating, these tough tactical transport aircraft could be the only means of sowing AP and AT mines to defeat border incursions or guerrilla forces. It is an aspect of SM delivery that merits closer examination. But one form of dispenser to receive considerable attention of late is the missile. No doubt as a consequence of developments such as FOFA or Airland Battle doctrine, and in recognition of the extreme hazards to be faced by manned aircraft penetrating enemy air space, the possibility of employing missiles to deliver submunitions has been the subject of much study. Of particular interest are the concepts based upon air-launched, stand-off missiles, which require an aircraft to deliver the missile to within 50 kilometres of the target. The missile then makes its own way to the target area, dispensing its weapon load near the target before crashing empty. Several systems are being proposed both in Europe and USA. The Franco-German study involves a Short Range Stand Off System (SR – SOM) to engage mobile armoured units. Dornier are pursuing a private venture, air to ground missile with a 20–25 kilometre range to meet this requirement. A 4-nation, feasibility study is taking place within NATO on a different system known as the Low Cost Powered Dispenser (LOCPOD), which is intended for use in the 1990s. This would be aimed at stationary targets at a distance of 35 kilometres, and one of its sub-munitions would be area denial minelets. In the US, a variety of stand-off systems are being developed to meet a possible USAF operational requirement, including the General Dynamics Medium Range Air to Surface Missile (MRASM) and Brunswick Corporation's Low Altitude Dispenser (LAD). A further candidate for this programme is the MBB/Matra Apache: a modular, air to ground weapon dispenser with a broad application against ground targets. Missile dispensers will both fulfil the demands of FOFA type doctrine and prove to be a more survivable and accurate means of deep interdiction than piloted aircraft. They are an ideal means of delivering mines remotely and this appears to be one of the major tasks for which they are envisaged.

No matter how mines and delivery systems develop in the future, mine warfare will continue to provide a challenge to the logistic services. Vast tonnages of mines will need to be outloaded from depots to engineer mine dumps, to helicopter bases, to artillery gun lines and to airfields. Once unpacked and issued to combat engineers or fitted into dispensers, the mines may take very little time to emplace, if all the projected improvements to laying and delivery systems materialize. However, these innovative and effective developments will be invalidated if the mines do not arrive in time to be put into use. Parallel improvements in the logistic chain must match those in mine warfare. Some progress is already visible. The British Army is adopting a heavy load delivery system known as DROPS (demountable rack off-loading and pick-up system) coupled to a new load handling system (LHS). The US Army is examining a similar system, known as Ampliroll. An alternative concept has recently arrived in the form of TILOS, the Tangram Integrated Logistic System. This is a twin unit, offering a fully mobile means of container delivery. The main part of the unit is the towed container body, mounted on a high mobility, cross-country suspension. The towing unit is a 4×4 protected tractor. Both elements can be provided with aluminium armour, that can be reinforced with Kevlar plates. Whilst DROPS is ideal for delivery from depot to a forward rendezvous (RV), TILOS is better suited for rapid delivery of stores and ammunition from a roadside RV directly to dispersed units in the battle area. These advances in logistic equipment are a welcome enhancement to the ability of combat services to supply the enormous quantities of mines and ammunition that a modern force requires, quantities that are unlikely to reduce drastically in the foreseeable future.

So far, the scope for improvements in mine warfare have been discussed primarily in equipment terms. Undoubtedly, there are similar opportunities to be pursued in the area of tactics and the subsequent employment of mines. For example, what benefits might accrue from the laying of several thin minefields, rather than one deep barrier? A useful study might be into the improved effectiveness of mines when supported by smoke, which could itself be generated by smoke mines. The reduced visibility could lead to an increased delay factor and more casualties as the men or vehicles flounder in the smoke. Provided the latter was not an IR screen composition, defending weapons equipped with TI sights could continue to engage the enemy caught in the mined area. As the cost of military equipment increases, and mines will not be excluded from this tendency, it is unlikely that defence budgets will grow to allow the purchase of all those items that become available, or are specified as operational requirements. It is probable that fewer, but more effective, weapons will have to be purchased and, in some instances, capabilities will be dropped through a lack of funding. With these pressures on defence votes, it is essential that existing stores and equipments are employed to best effect. This will be accomplished by a regular re-assessment of tactical concepts to ensure that the most effective use of men and material is achieved. A review of mine warfare techniques, as outlined above, should form part of any such appraisal. Yet new threats will emerge that can not be countered with existing resources, no matter how innovative a defender might be, and an original response will have to be developed. As an example, there is no reliable method at present for ground forces to destroy RPV or terrain-hugging, cruise missiles. The bounds of military technology are virtually limitless, and an anti-RPV or anti-cruise missile mine is entirely feasible. Perhaps these will be the priority projects, not of the third, but of the fourth generation mine programmes. Or will that privilege go to anti-satellite and anti-ballistic missile mines, sown as a barrier across the vastness of space?

Mines have been and remain effective, if under-rated, obstacles to the passage of both men and machines. Like physical fitness and prowess with personal weapons, mine warfare is an oft neglected aspect of combat efficiency, the importance of which only becomes apparent in war. Regrettably, it is difficult to reveal the potential of mines and counter-measures in peace, as their value can never be set in strong relief during those exercises, parades or exhibitions, which colour and influence the perceptions of decision makers. Yet past experience has amply demonstrated the worth of mines in battle, especially during those final moments when the enemy closes on to defensive positions. It is then that the mine has a devastating impact, inflicting casualties and breaking the momentum of the assault, whilst raising the morale and strengthening the resolve of the defender. But mines are more than a close protection weapon. They have become an essential component of combat attrition, with the task of reducing an opponent's strength throughout the whole battle area. Consequently, mines form an integral part of many operational plans and defensive tactics, to such an extent that considerable resources have been devoted to the development of suitable counter-measures. There is a general imbalance in favour of the mine over counter-mine techniques at present and this will continue for the foreseeable future, although the situation can change rapidly at the local level, when a determined breaching operation is put into effect. Mine warfare has altered considerably from the formative days of World War II. Nevertheless, its tactics, techniques and equipment are liable to face as much change in the future. It is to be hoped that the proven utility of the mine will continue to be recognized as a significant element in the land battle. If this should not be the case, and funds are diverted into more fashionable, if less cost-effective weapons, an unpleasant surprise may be in store for those forces who follow this course. It will be too late to acknowledge the need for mines or counter-measures during the ferment of war, when an enemy faces no hindrance to movement, or friendly forces are thwarted by the simplest of minefields. The foundation for a successful mine warfare capability has to be laid well in advance of the time that it may be required. Perhaps this book can act as a suitable blueprint for that foundation.

A Glossary of Mine Warfare Terms

Anti-lift device. A device arranged to detonate the mine to which it is attached, or to detonate another mine or charge nearby, if the mine is disturbed.

Anti-disturbance device. A device designed to detonate the mine to which it is attached if the mine is disturbed.

Armed mine. A mine from which all safety devices have been withdrawn and, after laying, all automatic safety features and/or arming delays have operated. Such a mine is ready to receive a target signal, influence or contact.

Arming. As applied to explosives, the changing from a safe condition to a state of readiness for initiation.

Arming delay device. A device fitted in a mine to prevent it being actuated for a preset time after laying.

Axial mining. Continuous or intermittent nuisance mining in great depth along the axis of enemy advance.

Booby trap. An explosive or non-explosive device or other material, deliberately placed to cause casualties when an unsuspecting person disturbs an apparently harmless object or performs a normally safe act.

Booby trapped mine. A mine laid with an anti-lift device.

Booster. A high-explosive element sufficiently sensitive so as to be actuated by small explosive elements in a fuze or primer and powerful enough to cause detonation of the main explosive filling.

Breaching. The employment of any available means to secure a passage through an enemy minefield or fortification.

Clearing or clearance operation. An operation designed to clear all mines from a route or area.

Cluster. A component of a pattern laid minefield. It may be anti-tank, anti-personnel, or mixed. It consists of one to five mines but no more than one anti-tank mine.

Density. The average number of mines per metre of minefield front.

Disarmed mine. A mine which has been rendered inoperative by breaking a link in the firing sequence.

Fuze. In mine warfare an igniter in which the actuating mechanism and detonator are all contained.

Horizontal action mine. A mine designed to produce a destructive effect in a plane approximately parallel to the ground. (*See* **Off Route Mine**)

Igniter. A device for actuating the charge in a mine, to which a detonator and booster charge must be fitted before the assembly is placed in the fuze well of the mine.

Irregular outer edge (IOE). Short mine strips laid in an irregular manner in front of a minefield facing the enemy, to deceive the enemy as to the type or extent of the minefield.

Land mine warfare. The strategic and tactical use of mines and their counter-measures.

Marker, lane. Used to mark a minefield lane. Lane markers at the entrance to, and exit from, the lane will be referenced to a landmark or intermediate marker.

Marking, minefield perimeter. Visible marking of the boundary of a minefield and indicating its extent.

Mine. An explosive or material, normally encased, designed to destroy or damage ground vehicles, boats, or aircraft, or designed to wound, kill or otherwise incapacitate personnel. It may be detonated by the action of its victim, by the passage of time, or by controlled means.

Mine, anti-personnel. A mine designed to cause casualties to personnel.

Mine, anti-tank. A mine designed to immobilize or destroy a tank.

Mine, area. A mine which is not dependent on the "shadow" of a target for actuation, but will sense and attack the target from a distance once it is within the mine's area of operation.

Mine, chemical. A mine containing a chemical agent designed to kill, injure or incapacitate personnel or to contaminate material or terrain.

Mine clearance. The process of detecting and/or removing land mines by manual or mechanical means.

Mine detector. In general, any instrument or method for the discovery of mines. Specifically, the electronic device which reacts to the presence of metal.

Mine, drill. An inert-filled mine, or mine-like body, used in loading, laying or discharge practice and trials.

Mine, inert. An inert replica of a standard mine. It is used for instructional purposes.

Mine, practice. A replica of a standard mine, having the same features and weight as the mine it represents. It is constructed to emit a puff of smoke or make a noise to simulate detonation.

Mine, river. A mine which is laid underwater in rivers and inland waterways, which are non-tidal, in order to attack floating and wading vehicles and equipment.

Mine row. A single row of mines or clusters.

Mines, scatterable. A mine laid without regard to classical pattern that is designed to be delivered by aircraft, artillery, missile, ground dispenser or hand thrown.

Minefield. An area of ground containing mines laid with or without pattern.

Minefield, anti-personnel. A minefield laid primarily for protection against infantry attack.

Minefield, anti-tank. A minefield laid primarily to cause tank casualties.

Minefield gap. A portion of a minefield in which no mines have been laid, of specified width to enable a friendly force to pass through the minefield in tactical formation.

Minefield lane. A marked lane, unmined or cleared of mines, leading through a minefield.

Minefield, mixed. A minefield containing both anti-tank and anti-personnel mines.

Minefield, nuisance. A minefield laid to delay and disorganize the enemy and to hinder his use of an area or route.

Minefield, phoney. An area of ground used to simulate a minefield with the object of deceiving the enemy.

Minefield, protective. A minefield employed to assist a unit in its local close-in protection.

Minefield record. A complete written record of all pertinent information concerned with a minefield, submitted on a standard form by the officer in charge of the laying operations.

Minefield report. A tactical report on the siting, progress or completion of a minefield.

Minefield, tactical. A minefield which is part of a formation obstacle plan and is laid to delay, channel or break up an enemy advance. Wherever possible it will be sited to enable direct or indirect fire to cover the mined area.

Neutralization. A mine is said to be neutralized when it has been rendered, by external means, incapable of firing on passage of a target, although it may remain dangerous to handle.

Pattern laying. The laying of mines in a fixed relationship to each other.

Off route mine. A mine usually set to fire horizontally at a passing target.

Prodding. A method of mine detection, using a sharp-pointed instrument to locate the mine by feel.

Random or scattered mine laying. The laying of mines without regard to pattern.

Recovery. The lifting, or clearance, of a minefield with the aid of any available minefield record.

Reactive mining. The act of emplacing mines at short notice, probably at a distance, and in previously unplanned locations.

Standard pattern. The agreed pattern to which mines are normally laid.

Undetectable. Mines are said to be undetectable when, by virtue of their construction, they cause no reaction in an electronic mine detector, or in other means of detection.

List of Abbreviations

AD	Anti-disturbance (fuze)
ADAM	Area Denial Artillery Munition
ADM	Atomic Demolition Munition
ADP	Automatic Data Processing
ADR	Airfield Damage Repair
ADW	Area Defence Weapon
AFV	Armoured Fighting Vehicle
AP	Anti Personnel
APC	Armoured Personnel Carrier
AT	Anti-tank
ATGW	Anti-tank Guided Weapon
AVLB	Armoured Vehicle Launched Bridge
AVRE	Armoured Vehicle Royal Engineers
C^3I	Command, Control, Communications and Information
CATFAE	Catapult Launched FAE
CET	Combat Engineer Tractor
CLAM	Clear Lane Marking System
CNR	Combat Net Radio
COV	Counter-obstacle Vehicle
DI	Double Impulse (fuze)
DDM	Direct Delivery Mine
DROPS	Demountable Rack Off-loading and Pick-up System
EFP	Explosion Formed Projectile
ELKE	Elevated Kinetic Energy Weapons System
EMP	Electro-magnetic Pulse/Engineer Mine Plough
EOD	Explosive Ordnance Disposal
ERAM	Extended Range Anti-armour Munition
EW	Electronic Warfare
FAE (or FAX)	Fuel Air Explosive
FASCAM	Family of Scatterable Mines
FEBA	Forward Edge of the Battle Area
FGA	Fighter Ground Attack
FOFA	Follow On Force Attack
FOO	Forward Observation Officer
FWA	Full Width Attack
FWMP	Full Width Mine Plough

GEMSS	Ground Emplaced Mine Scattering System
HE	High Explosive
HEAT	High Explosive Anti-tank
HE MMS	Hand Emplaced Minefield Marking Set
HF	High Frequency
IED	Improvised Explosive Device
IFV	Infantry Fighting Vehicle
IR	Infra-red
LAD	Low Altitude Dispenser
LAR	Light Artillery Rocket
LAW	Light Anti-tank Weapon
LHS	Load Handling System
LOCPOD	Low Cost Powered Dispenser
LVT	Landing Vehicle Tracked
MBT	Main Battle Tank
MCRS	Mine Clearance Roller System
MHE	Mechanical Handling Equipment
MMW	Millimetre Wave
MOPMS	Modular Pack Mine System
NATO	North Atlantic Treaty Organization
OP	Observation Post
ORM	Off-route Mine(s)
RAAMS	Remote Anti-armour Mine System
RAOC	Royal Army Ordnance Corps
RDF	Rapid Deployment Force
RDM	Remotely Delivered Mine(s)
RE	Royal Engineers
RPV	Remotely Piloted Vehicle
RV	Rendezvous
SAU	Safety and Arming Unit
SFF	Self Forging Fragment
SI	Single Impulse (fuze)
SLUFAE	Surface Launched Unit FAE
SM	Scatterable Mine(s)
SR-SOM	Short Range Stand Off Missile
TACOM	Tank Automotive Command
TI	Thermal Imagery
TV	Television
TWMP	Track Width Mine Plough
VDU	Visual Display Unit
VEMASID	Vehicle Magnetic Signature Duplicator
VHF	Very High Frequency
VSTOL	Vertical, Short Take-off and Landing
WWI	World War I
WWII	World War II

Bibliography

Textbook on Fortification, etc	Colonel G. Philips RE Pardon & Sons London (1899)
Fortress	Ian V. Hogg Macdonald & Jane's
A History of Greek Fire and Gunpowder	J. R. Partington W. Heffer & Sons
History of the Corps of Royal Engineers Vol. VIII and IX (1938–48)	Major-General R. P. Pakenham-Walsh Institution of Royal Engineers
The Royal Engineers	Derek Boyd Leo Cooper Ltd.
The Battle of Kursk	Major-General I. Paratkin Progress Publishers
Small Arms, Artillery and Special Weapons of the Third Reich	T. Gander and P. Chamberlain Macdonald and Jane's
The Challenge of War	G. Hartcup David and Charles
Vanguard of Victory	D. Fletcher HMSO
The Funnies	G. W. Futter Model and Allied Publications
Encyclopedia of Tanks	D. Crow and R. J. Ecks Barrie and Jenkins
Elusive Victory	Colonel T. N. Dupoy Macdonald and Jane's

The Arab-Israeli Wars   Chaim Herzog
                                                       Arms and Armour Press

Mounted Combat in Vietnam   General D. A. Starry
                                                       US Govt. Printing Office

Vietnam Tracks: Armour in Battle 1945–75   S. Dunstan
                                                       Osprey

The Battle for the Falklands   M. Hastings and S. Jenkins
                                                       Michael Joseph

Weapons and War Machines   A. Kershaw and I. Close
                                                       Phoebus

Anti Personnel Weapons   SIPRI
                                                       Taylor and Francis Ltd

Brassey's Infantry Weapons of the World   J. I. H. Owen
                                                       Brassey's

Weapons and Tactics of the Soviet Army   D. C. Isby
                                                       Jane's

Jane's Military Vehicles and Ground Support   C. F. Foss and T. J. Gander
Equipment 1984 Fifth Edition   Jane's

Ammunition (including Grenades and Mines)   K. J. W. Goad and D. H. J. Halsey
                                                       Brassey's

MAGAZINE ARTICLES

Anti Tank Mines in Mobile Warfare   Captain R. H. Dewing
                                                       R. E. Journal
                                                       March 1924
                                                       (Republished March 1974)

The Development of Land Mine Warfare   Major-General B. K. Young
                                                       The Army Quarterly
                                                       January and April 1945

Some Thoughts on Minewarfare   Major J. C. N. Jatar
                                                       Journal of the United Service
                                                       Institution of India
                                                       September 1966

Minbotrap (Mines and Booby Traps in Vietnam)

Lieutenant-Colonel R. E. Mack
Marine Corps Gazette
July 1967

Port Stanley Minefields

Captain J. G. Mullin RE
British Army Review
No. 75 December 1983

Explosive Ordnance Disposal: The British Organization against the Bomber

International Law Enforcement
Vol. 1, No. 4, 1984

Modern Land Mine Warfare

K. Alder
Armada International
November/December 1980

Mines in Land Warfare

C. F. Foss
Defence
April 1979

Land Mine Warfare: The British Position

T. J. Gander
Jane's Defence Review 1983

The Underground World of the Land Mine

T. J. Gander
Jane's Military Review
1983/84

Key Weapons: Landmines

War in Peace
No. 100 1984

Minefields: New orientations for their utilization

W. Schnaufer
Defence Today
February 1985

Land Mine Technology Today

I. V. Hogg
Defence
March 1981

Aspects of Land-Mine Warfare

Strategic Review
March 1984

Aggressive Development Program Improves Mine Warfare Capacity

A. R. Nunes-Vais
Defence Management Journal
October 1974

Mines-Restricting the Enemy's Movements

Major R. Stampfer
Soldat und Technik
2/1981

Landmines	A. von Tresckow *Soldat und Technik* 8/1975
Land Mine Warfare and Conventional Deterrence	J. F. Rybicki *NATO's Sixteen Nations* Vol. **29** Issue 5 September/October 1984
The Mined Obstacle in American Tactical Doctrine	L. Golino and A. Grimaldi *Defence Today* No. 59–60
Mine Warfare Equipment	*Jane's Defence Weekly* 7 July 1984
Equipment for Military Engineers	*Defence Material* September/October 1984
Battle Baffles or Obstacles on the European Battlefield	Major C. E. E. Sloan *Royal Engineers Journal* Vol. **97** No. 3 September 1983
Soviet Mine Warfare: Army's "Silent Death"	Lieutenant-Colonel W. P. Baxter *Army* July 1982
Soviet Land Mine Warfare	B. F. Halloran *The Military Engineer* Vol. **64** No. 418 March/April 1972
Combat Engineers of the Soviet Army	C. N. Donnelly *International Defence Review* Special Series No. 16
The Soviet Armoured Minelayer GMZ	*Soldat und Technik* 10/1981
Soviet Armoured Mineclearers	*Soldat und Technik* 3/1972
Engineer Capabilities of the Soviet and WP Armies	J. E. Deaton *Military Engineer* November/December 1979

Soviet Tactics for Overcoming NATO Anti-Tank Defences

C. N. Donnelly
International Defense Review
7/1979

Installation of Minefields at Night

V. Voucharov
Voyennyy Vestnik
No. 2 1982 (USSR)

Reconnaissance of Mines and Explosive Obstacles

Colonel B. Varenyshav
Voennye Zvaniya
No. 10 1972 (USSR)

Anti-Personnel Mines: Armaments for Mass Application

Front
November 1981 (Yugoslavia)

A Trap for Armoured Vehicles

M. Ljujic
Klopka Za Oklopna Vozila
December 1982 (Yugoslavia)

Helicopter Emplaced Mines

Shi Yongli
Hankong Zhishi
Issue 132 (China)

Antitank Mines
Parts: I; II; III

G. Backofen and L. W. Williams
Armour
July/August; September/October;
November/December 1981

Anti-Tank Mines of the Second Generation

Lieutenant-Colonel P. Crevecoeur
Armada International
January/February 1984

Anti-Tank Mines

Military Technology and Economics
July 1981

A New Anti-Tank Mine (XM56)

A. R. Nunes-Vais
National Defense
November/December 1974

The FFV 028 Anti-Tank Mine

Lieutenant-Colonel P. Crevecoeur
International Defence Review
3/1977

Microprocessor Controls Antitank Skeet

P. J. Klass
Aviation Week and Space Technology
22 March 1982

The Use of Intelligent Ammunition in AT Defence

K. Adler
Armada International
5/1983

Stopping Mass Tank Attacks

J. Rybicki
Military Technology
March 1984

Combat Engineer Equipment for the 1980s

Colonel B. C. Hughes
Military Engineer
November/December 1979

Europe's Pipe Mines

Jane's Defence Weekly
22 September 1984

Get Smart Munitions

C. R. Seashore
Defense Electronics
May 1984

Modern Methods of the Attack of Armour

P. N. Jones
Metallurgist and Materials Technologist
September 1984

New Armour-Plating Materials in France

P. Mercillon
Defence and Armament
June 1984

Tank Technology in the USA

P. L. Balte
Defence Attache
5/1984

The Leopard 3 Debated

W. Mathos and R. Hilmes
Military Technology
10/1984

Merkava Mark 2

R. M. Ogorkiewicz
International Defence Review
3/1985

The Soviet Helicopter on the Battlefield

C. N. Donnelly
International Defense Review
5/1984

Flying Tanks?

R. Simpkin
Military Technology
8/1984

Tank Delivered Scatterable Mines   M. A. Andrews
                                                  Military Review
                                                  December 1978

A Unique New Capacity: Scatterable Mines   M. B. Chase
                                                  *Army Research, Development and
                                                  Acquisition*
                                                  March/April 1980

Scatterable Mines   Major M. L. Howell
                                                  The Military Engineer
                                                  November/December 1977

Scatterable Mines: Superweapon?   P. W. McDavitt
                                                  National Defense
                                                  September/October 1979

Scatterable Land Mines   Lieutenant-Colonel R. A. Riaz
                                                  Pakistan Army Journal
                                                  December 1982

The Case against Tank Delivered Scatterable   Major G. F. Rogers
Mines   *Military Review*
                                                  December 1979

Scatterable Mines: The New Anti-Mobility   Lieutenant Colonel N. M. White
Weapon for the 1980s   *Royal Engineers Journal*
                                                  March 1979

Helicopter-Dropped Mine Developed   L. Yaffee
                                                  *Aviation Week and Space
                                                  Technology*
                                                  28 April 1975

The MW-1 Sub-Munition Dispenser   *NATO's Sixteen Nations*
                                                  Special Issue 2/1984

MW-1 — The Multi-Purpose Weapon System   W. Flume
                                                  Military Technology
                                                  Vol. **IX** Issue 2 1985

SLUFAE: Long-Range Minefield Breaching   J. A. Dennis
System Test   *Army Research and Development*
                                                  May/June 1976

Countermeasures Against Mines and Booby   Major W. M. Greene
Traps   *Army Journal*
                                                  June 1970

Minefield Breaching

Lieutenant-Colonel J. Kitching
International Defense Review
June 3/1977

Defeat of Tactical Minefields

J. N. Marsden
National Defense
September/October 1975

Landmines and Countermeasures

Military Technology and Economics
April/May 1980

Mining and Counter-mining: Paths to the Future

R. Pengelley
Defence Attache
1/1982

Dogs in Countermine Warfare

Captain W. L. Quinn
Infantry
July/August 1971

TACOM Builds Mine-Clearing Vehicles

Army Research, Development and Acquisition Magazine
July/August 1984

Land Mines: Detection and Countermeasures

Lieutenant-Colonel L. Golino
Defence Today
August 1984

Israeli Mine Plough

International Defence Review
5/1985

Submunitions pose a tough disposal task

M. Daly
Jane's Defence Weekly
15 June 1985

Modernising Combat Engineering Capabilities

J. Reed
Defence Minister and Chief of Staff
No. 2/1985

Mine Flails Are Back

T. J. Gander
Jane's Defence Weekly
23 February 1985

Mines and Mine Clearance

Colonel N. L. Dodd (Retd.)
Asian Defence Journal
12/1983

The British Army's New Mine Plough

M. Hewish
International Defense Review
5/1984

Mine Countermeasures Hovercraft

A. Blunden
International Defense Review
6/1983

Remote Control of Earthmoving Equipment

Captain C. E. E. Sloan
Royal Engineers Journal
Vol. **93** No. 1 March 1979

Modular C3I

M. J. Gething
Defence
November 1984

C3I's Role on the Battlefield

Defence Electronics
October 1984

The Ptarmigan System

C. Warren
International Defense Review
Special Electronics No. 1/1984

BATES — A Revolution in the Control of Artillery

Major C. E. E. Sloan
Electronics and Power
Vol. **27** No. 7/8 July/August 1981

Chips Keep the Generals in Shape

Colonel P. Pengelley
Defence Attache
5/1984

Digital Terrain Modelling

P. Thompson
Defence, Communications and Security Review
2/1984

Terrain Evaluation on Land and Underwater

K. C. Wyatt and E. W. Cookson
Defence, Communications and Security Review
1/1985

Surveillance and Reconnaissance for the Airland Battle

J. Rybicki
Military Technology
Vol. **IX** Issue 2 1985

Emerging Technologies and the Airland Battle

J. F. Rybicki
Military Technology
10/1984

Robotic Mobile Mines Facilitate Airland Battle 2000 Tactics

C. W. Nelson, D. Baskett, J. Kirsch
Defense Systems Review
November 1983

Attacking Targets Beyond the FEBA

M. Hewish
International Defense Review
8/1984

Advanced Stand-Off Missiles for Strike Aircraft

Military Technology
Vol. **IX** Issue 3 1985

MILITARY REFERENCES

German Land Mines

General Headquarters
1918 (UK)

German Traps and Mines

SME Fortification Circular No. 57
1 March 1919

Minefield Records

Chief Engineer 8th Army
Engineer Directive No. 2
24 September 1942

German Mines and Traps

Enemy Equipment Part I
1943

Japanese Mines and Demolition Equipment

Enemy Equipment Part III
1945

Mine Detectors

Canadian Military HQ London
9 November 1945

Minefield Clearance and Casualties

Military Operational Research Unit
Report No. 7 May 1946

Mine Clearance and Detection

Assault Training and Development Centre
1944

Notes on the Protection of Floating Bridges against Mines and Debris

Ministry of Supply
February 1945

Field Works in Winter Warfare

Defence Commissariat Moscow
1945

Mines, Mine Detectors and Demolition Equipment	*Illustrated Record of German Army Equipment 1939–45* Vol. **V** MI 10 The War Office 1947
Recognition of Land Mines	MI 10 The War Office 1951
Anti-Mine and other special defensive and offensive devices associated with AFV's	Fighting Vehicles Design Establishment March 1951
Mines and Booby Traps used in Korea	*HQ 8th US Army Korea Office of the Engineer 1951*
Land Minewarfare	*Department of the Army Training Circular No. 34* 14 November 1952
User Handbook for Shoes Anti Mine	War Office Code No. 10964 December 1954
Minewarfare Booklet	1st Australian Task Force August 1969
VC and NVA Employment of Mines and Booby Traps	Technical Intelligence Branch Combined Intelligence Center Vietnam
Handbook of Land Service Ammunition	Army Code 60525 1971
Handbook of Ammunition	Royal Military College of Science October 1981
Defence in the Land Battle	Colonel M. G. L. Robert MBE 1974/75 Defence Fellow Kings College London University
Mines in the Falkland Islands	*RSME Handbook* November 1982
Landmine and Countermine Warfare *Eastern Europe* *Western Europe* *North Africa 1940–43* *Italy 1943–44* *Korea 1950–54* *Vietnam 1964–69*	*Engineer Agency for Resources Inventories Washington DC*

Mine/Countermine Operations at the Company Level	FM 20–32 HQ Department of the Army 1976
Foreign Mine Warfare Equipment	TM 5–280 US Department of the Army July 1971
Mine and Trap Clearance	*Military Engineering* Vol. II *Field Engineering* *Pamphlet No. 5 1968* *TRADOC Pamphlet* 525–19 18 June 1982
Minelaying	*Military Engineering* Vol. **II** *Field Engineering* *Pamphlet* No. 5 1982
Student Handbook	Euro NATO Training Engineer Course German Army Engineer School Munich

STANAG 2036 Land Minefield Laying Marking Recording and Reporting Procedures

STANAG 2096 Reporting Engineer Information in the Field

Photograph Credits

Index

151